CONTENTS

Edited by Tony Lynch.
Designed by Sue Bartram and Melanie Clayden.
Illustrations by Simon Girling Associates.

Published by
Grandreams Limited
Jadwin House, 205-211 Kentish Town Road
London NW5 2JU

Printed in Belgium

£5.50

FIVE GO ON TV

The Famous Five have never gone out of fashion. The books by Enid Blyton are still read as avidly as ever by children all over the world. And now there's a brand new thirteen episode TV series to enjoy, featuring Julian, George, Dick, Anne and, of course, Timmy the dog...

FIVE FILMING FACTS

It took six months of searching all over Britain to find the right actors. Hundreds of schools were visited and drama workshops were held before the final choices were made.

Kirrin Island is actually two places hundreds of miles apart. A suitable island couldn't be found, so technological tricks were used. The island is actually a peninsular off the coast of North Devon and the castle is Dunstanburgh in the North East of England. On screen the combined result is 'Kirrin Island' – and it works!

Paul Child who plays 'Dick' messed up his audition – even though he was already an experienced actor!

Jemima Rooper who plays 'George' didn't want her hair cut for the part!

Connal who plays 'Timmy' the dog took one scene too seriously. He mistakenly thought a 'villian' was really attacking 'George' – and ripped the actor's trousers!

The TV adventures, co-produced by Zenith North and Portman Productions, are packed with non-stop action, with The Famous Five up against all manner of perils from smugglers and spies, to thieves and blackmailers.

Then there are secret tunnels, cryptic messages, lost gold and stolen diamonds!

But as all Famous Five fans know, the four children and their dog are more than a match for any wrongdoer. They cleverly find ways to outsmart the criminals and help to catch them.

You'll be thrilled by the spectacular backdrops to the adventures: a ruined castle and haunted house, an old lighthouse and a spooky deserted island.

The series is set in 1953, as it was thought that children deserved to see the work of Enid Blyton as she wrote it. Yet, the stories are as up-to-date as ever, because they are such rattling good adventures.

One of the most difficult jobs before the series could begin, was finding the actors to portray the Famous Five. The response from the public was overwhelming. "I think every

The Famous Five set off on an adventure

ENID BLYTON ... AN AMAZING AUTHOR!

Enid Blyton's first Famous Five book, 'Five On A Treasure Island', was published in 1942.

She wrote 21 adventure stories of The Famous Five.

The Famous Five books are still best-sellers and have never been out of print.

She has been one of the most prolific children's authors of the 20th century. She wrote hundreds of stories of mystery, school, adventure – as well as for younger children with stories such as 'Noddy'.

8 million of Enid Blyton's books are bought around the world every year. Enid Blyton has become one of the most popular children's authors of all time. Her books are translated into more than 30 languages.

child in the country wanted to take part," says producer John Price. "We had sacks of letters from children, parents, neighbours and teachers."

Hundreds and hundreds of children were seen. Finally, four lucky youngsters and a dog were chosen for the main roles. Fourteen-year-old Marco Williamson from Amersham portrays Julian; thirteen-year-old Jemima Rooper from Fulham plays George; thirteen-year-old Paul Child from High Wycombe plays Dick; eleven-year-old Laura Petela from Bath is Anne and five-year-old Connal plays Timmy the dog.

It helped that all four children were fans of The Famous Five as they were already familiar with the characters and storylines.

Enid Blyton's daughter, Gillian Baverstock, was involved in the TV adaptation throughout and was really happy when she saw the new Famous Five in their costumes for the

first time. "If only my mother could have seen them – they're perfect," she said.

The shooting of the thirteen episodes was done on a three months schedule.

The young actors were in almost every scene so it was tough going. Under law, children are only allowed to work a certain number of hours a day and when filming finished, school work had to be done.

But the youngsters loved every minute of the filming, of course, and they won further approval from Gillian Baverstock. "Their concentration, focus and sheer professionalism is astonishing. I'm so delighted with it all and I know my mother would have been equally impressed."

Marco, Jemima, Paul, Laura and Connal are certain to find success with their appearances. Like Enid Blyton's books, The Famous Five TV adventures will be enjoyed by people in their millions!

5

JULIAN

"Julian is not like me at all!"

Julian is the leader of The Famous Five, and the elder brother of Dick and Anne. A very confident and reliable boy, he can be counted on to think up a plan for getting out of any tricky situation. He's tall and physically strong, which comes in useful. A no-nonsense type who likes straight talking, Julian doesn't suffer fools gladly!

says Marco Williamson

THE FAMOUS FIVE™

* Marco has worked with some of Britain's top actors in Shakespeare's 'Richard III'

* Marco's favourite sport is cross-country running, which explains all his energy!

Julian defends himself!

Just like Julian, Marco is a natural leader. That was one reason why he was chosen for the role. His looks, height and energy also made him just right. Marco admires the character he plays, "Julian takes responsibility. He's the older brother, so he keeps Dick in line and looks after his sister Anne."

But keeping up with Julian's high standards in real life is a bit trickier for Marco. "Julian is sensible and he believes in setting a good example." Maybe he's being modest, but Marco doesn't think that description resembles him.

After winning the part, Marco learnt that his fashionable locks had to be shorn. "I hated it!" says Marco. "The first thing I did afterwards was to go and buy a cap!"

For a fourteen-year-old, Marco is remarkably confident. Perhaps that's because he is an experienced actor who has worked for the Royal National Theatre. Yet even he found the making of the TV series involved a lot of pressure, "When we weren't actually filming we had to learn all our lines as well as keep up with our school work!"

GEORGE

George is the thirteen-year-old cousin to Julian, Dick and Anne. At first, she can seem rude and difficult. But deep down she is kindhearted and loyal. Once a friend, always a friend. Lively and wiry, she's a very good swimmer and can row a boat strongly. She's a real tomboy who gets everyone to call her George. Call her by her proper name 'Georgina' and she won't answer!

George and good old Timmy!

THE FAMOUS FIVE™

* Jemima is a shopping fanatic!
* It took four hours to change Jemima's long straight hair into George's short curly style!

"I always wanted to be George," says Jemima Rooper

Even from an early age, Jemima Rooper wanted to be an actor. Her mother heard her say so time and again. When she was eight, Jemima decided it was time for action. So she arranged things herself, proving she was just as impulsive as George would be!

Telephoning an actors' agent, she made her own appointment! Her mum happily supported her and agreed to help Jemima attain her ambition.

Now thirteen-year-old Jemima is glad she made that phone call – because she's appearing in one of her favourite stories! "I loved all The Famous Five books," she says. "I like George because she's straightforward and a very loyal friend. She feels she has to prove she's as good as a boy."

Jemima looked forward to playing George, but was a little worried about the dramatic transformation of her hair. "I thought I would be really upset," she says. "But I was so relieved when it was all over that I laughed!"

Ask Jemima what she enjoyed most about making the series and she'll say, "Everything!"

THE FAMOUS FIVE™

An agile, cheeky thirteen-year-old action boy who can't resist adventure. Dick often has a twinkle in his eyes, which could mean he either has a joke to crack or he's up to some mischief!

"I joined The Famous Five Club when I was younger!"

says *Paul Child*

DICK

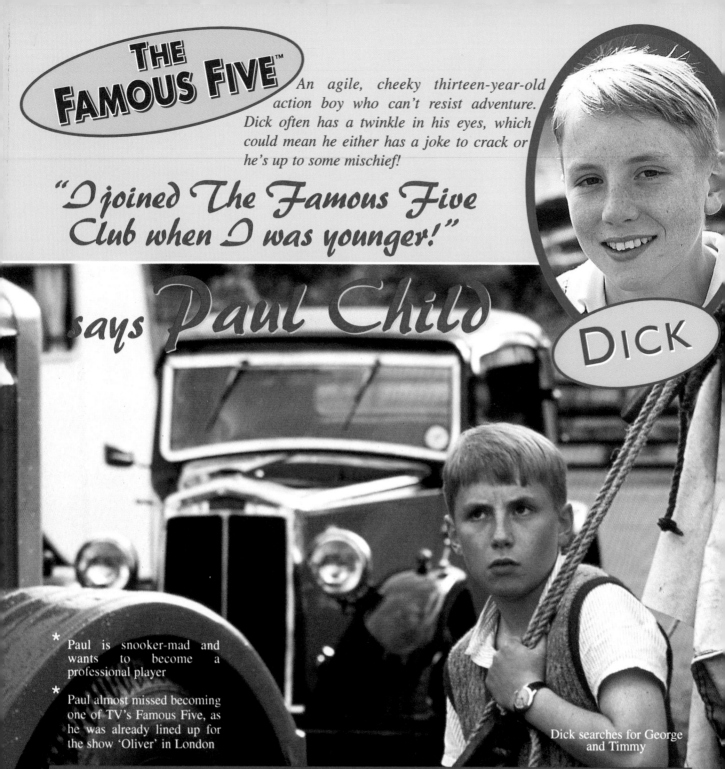

Dick searches for George and Timmy

* Paul is snooker-mad and wants to become a professional player

* Paul almost missed becoming one of TV's Famous Five, as he was already lined up for the show 'Oliver' in London

It was a disaster day for Paul Child when he made up his mind to attend a Famous Five workshop. He took a taxi and the driver got lost! When he eventually arrived for the audition, he was all hyped up and unable to perform properly. So much so that he fluffed his lines.

That was unusual for this thirteen-year-old, because Paul has considerable acting experience. It simply showed the tremendous importance he attached to getting the part.

"We walked him round the block to calm him down and he started again," says one of the producers. "We soon realised we had found 'Dick', Paul captures his personality perfectly!"

Paul was already familiar with The Famous Five. He had read all the books and had been a committed Famous Five Club member. He is similar to Dick in many ways – very outgoing and the joker of the pack!

He shares Dick's enthusiasm for adventure and challenges, "Dick is brave and he gets people out of trouble," says Paul.

There is one difference between Dick and Paul though. "He is sometimes sarcastic, which I'm not."

The only thing that Paul complained about during the filming was Dick's trousers – they itched like mad!

8

THE FAMOUS FIVE™

Anne in 'Five On A Secret Trail'

At 12-years-old Anne is the youngest of The Famous Five (apart from Timmy!). She's a pretty, pleasant girl who comes over as rather shy and timid at times. But Anne has an inner toughness and the 'softy' look is just a front!

"I would have loved to be Georgina"

says Laura Petela

ANNE

* Laura enjoys The Famous Five books so much, she's read some of them twice!

* Laura loves all animals and in particular her Shetland pony, Coco.

Not only had Laura Petela never thought about being Anne, she'd never even considered acting. "At school we were given leaflets about a drama workshop being organised by HTV," she explains. "I thought I'd give it a go and I really enjoyed it. Then I heard about the auditions for The Famous Five. At first I thought I'd do it for a laugh, but finally I decided I'd really go for it. I didn't really think I stood a chance, so I tried not to get too excited."

Although she had never acted professionally before, the makers of the TV series took one look at the slight, pretty girl and knew they had found their 'Anne'. "Laura can act really well, which is unusual for an eleven-year-old with no experience," said one Producer.

But there was a problem to begin with - Laura identified with George more than Anne. She wanted that part of the tomboyish cousin, as she thought Anne might be a bit soppy.

However, the Producers soon persuaded her otherwise and told her they didn't want Anne to be insipid anyway and she could be as strong-willed as George.

"Laura has bottle and attitude," says one Producer. "Although she's the youngest, she more than holds her own with the others."

Another thing in Laura's favour was the fact that she was an expert on the Famous Five stories. She's been reading them since the age of six and still enjoys them to this day.

Timmy is George's dog, she found him as a puppy on the moors. Far from being perfect-looking, Timmy's tail is too long and his ears stick up too much. It's impossible to tell what breed he is. But he's friendly and fun-loving and The Famous Five love him to bits. He has a strong bark and is very protective. He certainly will chase villains when asked!

...portrayed by Connal

THE FAMOUS FIVE™

* Connal is already a TV star! He's appeared in Peak Practice and Seaforth
* Connal was discovered in a dogs' home when he was very young

"Connal has his own particular method of acting," says his owner Gill Raddings. "The 'method' is to bribe him with his favourite treat and then he'll thank you with a star performance!"

Five-year-old Connal has been with Gill, a professional trainer of animals for the television and film industry, since he was 18-months-old. A docile and amiable dog, he showed an instinct for acting almost at once and has now built up a successful career.

Everyone working on The Famous Five TV series fell in love with Connal, and he formed a special bond with Jemima Rooper who plays his screen owner George.

Because he is so laid back, there was a worry that Connal wouldn't turn on the action when it came to confronting 'villains' on the sets.

In fact, the opposite happened! Connal literally leapt into the part, hurling himself at the nasties. Some of the actors thought Connal was perhaps getting too much into his screen persona as they ran for it!

Connal became like a true member of The Famous Five, getting very close to the young actors. "He used to go mad when he saw the children every morning," says Gill. "I couldn't do anything with him until he'd greeted them and calmed down."

A keen and dogged actor, Connal took lots of rests inbetween takes. After all, a dog doesn't have to learn lines like human actors!

When you watch The Famous Five on TV, you'll see Connal IS Timmy, and you'll be crazy about him, too!

Uncle Quentin

Christopher Good portrays George's father, and uncle of Julian, Dick and Anne. A clever and eccentric scientist, he frowns a lot and can become extremely angry – especially with George!

Aunt Frances

Mary Waterhouse plays George's mother, and aunt of Julian, Dick and Anne. She is patient and gentle, and an excellent cook. Her plum pies and ginger cakes are delicious and very popular with The Famous Five - that includes Timmy!

THE FAMOUS FIVE FILMS

The first time that The Famous Five were seen on film was in 1957 when 'Five On A Treasure Island' was shot in black and white by Rank Screen Services for the children's Saturday cinema programmes.

The film was shot near Swanage in Dorset, where Enid Blyton spent all her holidays. She stayed down there during much of the shooting and met all the actors and actresses taking part.

In 1963, the Children's Film Foundation made a second series of films out of 'Five Have A Mystery To Solve'. However, Enid Blyton did not watch the making of this as she was unwell.

In the early 1970s, a Danish film company made two full-length films using 'Five Go Adventuring Again' and 'Five Get Into Trouble'. Unfortunately, the child actors had grown too old by the following year and the boys' voices had broken, so no more were made.

In the late 1970s, the first Famous Five series was made for television. You may have seen this on video as it is still available. You will have noticed that the children wear the clothes of the '70s which look old-fashioned now. So with the present series it was decided to set the series in the early 1950s when the books were written. Now it will always look the way Enid Blyton imagined.

The children keep an eye on things

THE FAMOUS FIVE ON STAGE

Enid Blyton wrote a play about The Famous Five for the London theatre in 1955. It was performed in different theatres for two years and was very exciting. It was difficult to find theatres for the play because if the play was put on in the afternoon, the theatre management had to find another play for the evening. So the Noddy Pantomime was put on in the afternoons and The Famous Five in the evenings - but parents found it was too late for children, especially when school started.

In the Easter period of 1996, the King's Head Theatre in Islington put on a Famous Five musical that was specially written and based on 'Five Go Adventuring Again'. In January of 1997, the musical will tour to different theatres around the country. It keeps faithfully to the story and characters, while the music is so catchy, you can't help coming away singing. One strange coincidence – the girl who played Anne in the very first theatre production is now the wife of the writer of the music for the 1996 production!

Happy Christmas, Five!

Christmas Eve at Kirrin Cottage – and the Five were all there together! They were up in the boys' bedroom, packing Christmas presents in bright paper. Timmy was very excited, and nosed about the room, his long tail wagging in delight.

"Don't keep slapping my legs with your tail, Tim," said Anne. "Look out, George, he's getting tangled up with your ball of string!"

"Don't look round, Anne, I'm packing up your present," said Dick. "My word – there'll be a lot to give out this Christmas, with all of us here – and everyone giving everyone else something!"

"I've a B-O-N-E for Timmy," said Anne, "but it's downstairs in the larder. I was afraid he'd sniff it out up here."

"Woof," said Timmy, slapping his tail against Anne's legs again.

"He knows perfectly well that B-O-N-E spells bone," said Julian. "Now you've made him sniff all about my parcels! Timmy

12

– go downstairs, please!"

"Oh no – he does so love Christmas time, and helping us to pack up parcels," said George. "Sit, Timmy. SIT, I say. That's the third time you've knocked down my pile of presents."

Downstairs, her father and mother were packing up parcels, too. They seemed to have as many as the four cousins upstairs! Mrs. Kirrin looked at the pile of packages on the table.

"Far too many to go on the tree!" she said. "We'd better put all our parcels and the children's too into a sack, Quentin. We can stand the sack at the bottom of the tree, and you can be Father Christmas and hand them out tomorrow morning."

"I am NOT going to be Father Christmas," said Mr. Kirrin. "All this nonsense at Christmas time! Bits of paper everywhere – parcels to undo – Timmy barking his head off. Hark at him now! I shall go mad! He's to go to his kennel."

"No, no, Quentin – don't upset George on Christmas Eve," said Mrs. Kirrin. "Look – you go and sit down quietly in your study and read the paper. I'll finish the parcels. But you MUST be good and hand them out to the children tomorrow morning – yes, and hand Timmy's to him too."

Supper-time came all too soon that night. When the bell rang to tell the Five that the meal was ready, they groaned. "Have to finish afterwards," said Dick, looking round at the mess of parcels, paper, string, ribbon and labels. "Supper, Timmy, supper!"

Timmy shot downstairs at top speed, bumping heavily into Uncle Quentin, who was just coming out of his study. Timmy gave him a quick lick of apology, and ran into the dining-room, putting his front feet on the table to see what was there.

"Down, Timmy – what manners!" said Julian. "Hello, Uncle Quentin – done up all your parcels yet?"

His uncle grunted. Aunt Fanny laughed. "He's going to be Father Christmas tomorrow morning and hand out all the presents," she said. "Don't scowl like that, Quentin dear – you look just like George when I tell her to fetch something!"

"I do NOT scowl," said George, scowling immediately, of course. Everyone roared at her, and she had to smile.

"Christmas Day tomorrow," said Anne happily. "Aunt Fanny, it's lovely of you to have us all here for Christmas. Goodness, we'll never finish opening our parcels tomorrow morning! I've at least one for everybody, and so has everyone else."

"A nice little bit of arithmetic," said Julian. "That means we've about forty or more presents to undo – counting in those for Joanna, the cook, and Timmy."

"What a waste of time!" That remark came from Uncle Quentin, of course!

"It's a good thing you're not as horrid

as you pretend to be, Father," said George, and grinned at him. "You always look so fierce – and yet I bet you've been round the shops buying all kinds of things. Hasn't he, Mother? I bet he's bought Timmy something, too."

"Stop saying 'I bet'," said her father. "And don't put ideas in Timmy's head. Why on earth should I go shopping for him?"

"Woof!" said Timmy, from under the table, delighted to hear his name. He wagged his tail violently and Uncle Quentin leapt to his feet with a yell.

"Take that dog out! Slapping me with his tail like that! Why can't he have a short tail? I'll …"

"Sit down, Quentin," said his wife. "Timmy, come out. Sit over there. Now – let's change the subject!"

The four cousins looked at one another and grinned. It was lovely to be at Kirrin Cottage again, with dear kind Aunt Fanny, and quick-tempered Uncle Quentin. He was now beaming round at them,

offering them a second helping.

"No thanks," said Dick. "I'm saving up for the pudding. I spotted it in the larder – scrumptious!"

After supper they finished their parcels, and brought them all down to the sitting-room. The tree was there, looking very jolly, though the candles on it were not yet lighted. It was hung with tinsel and little sparkling ornaments, and had at the top the fairy doll that had been on every Christmas tree since George was little.

The parcels were put into a big sack, and this was set at the foot of the tree, ready for the morning. Timmy immediately went to sniff at it, from top to bottom.

"He can smell his Christmas bone," said Anne. "Timmy, come away. I won't have you guessing my present!"

They then played games, and Timmy joined in. He was so excited that he began to bark, and Uncle Quentin stormed out of his study at once, and appeared in the sitting-room.

"George! I've told you before I won't have Timmy barking in the house. Yes, I know it's Christmas Eve, but I can't STAND that barking. Why must he have such a loud one? It's enough to deafen me. I'll turn him out. He can go to his kennel!"

"Oh no, Father – not on Christmas Eve!" said George, horrified. "Timmy, go and lie down – and BE QUIET!"

"He's to go out to his kennel," said her father. "That's my last word. Out, Timmy, OUT!"

So out poor Timmy had to go, his tail well down. He felt puzzled. The children had been shouting, hadn't they? It was their way of barking. Well, why couldn't he shout in his own way, which was barking?

George was cross, and Anne was almost in tears. Poor Timmy – to be sent out to his kennel on Christmas Eve! She went to comfort George, and was surprised to see that she wasn't looking upset.

"Don't worry, Anne – I'll fetch him in when we go to bed and he can sleep in our room as usual," she said.

"You can't do that!" said Anne. "Uncle Quentin would be furious if he discovered him there."

"He won't," said George. "It's no good, Anne – I'm going to have Timmy with me tonight, though I KNOW I shouldn't. I couldn't bear not to. I'll own up to Father tomorrow."

So, when the household was safely in bed, George crept downstairs to fetch Timmy from his kennel. He whined softly in joy and wagged his big tail.

"Be quiet now," whispered George, and took him upstairs – quite forgetting to lock the kitchen door! Timmy settled down on the rug beside her bed, very happy, and soon Anne and George were fast asleep in their beds, while the two boys slept soundly in their room nearby.

All four were awakened by a terrific bout of barking from Timmy! He stood at the bedroom door, scraping at it, trying to open it, barking at the top of his voice!

George leapt out of bed in alarm.

"What is it, Timmy? What is it? Stop barking – Father will hear you and know you're in the house and not in your kennel. Oh DO shut up, Timmy!"

But by this time everyone was wide awake, and soon the whole household was out on the landing, alarmed. George's father was very angry when he saw that Timmy was in the house after all. "Why isn't he in his kennel? What's the matter with him? How DARE you disobey me, George?"

"Take him out to his kennel at once, George," said her mother, very cross too. "He's over-excited tonight – it was all that fun and games you had. Take him out at once."

"But, Mother – he doesn't usually bark. Perhaps there was a burglar in the house," said poor George.

"Nonsense!" said her father, angrily. "No burglar would come on Christmas Eve. Take the dog out to his kennel – and don't let me hear another sound tonight!"

"Go on, George, now," said her mother. "Do as you are told and don't spoil Christmas."

Timmy was very sad to be put into his kennel again. He whined dismally, and George almost made up her mind to stay outside with him. But his kennel was not big enough to take both of them, so she gave him a hug and went indoors with Anne, scowling in the darkness. This time she remembered to lock the door behind her! Soon everyone was in bed again, and sound asleep.

Anne awoke a little while later and sat up in bed. She had heard something – some noise downstairs. She sat and listened. Was there someone in the living-room? Then she heard a click. 'Like a door being shut,' she thought, and wondered if she should wake George. No – surely Timmy would bark loudly if he heard anything suspicious – he was only just outside, in his kennel. Perhaps he had

heard something when he had barked before.

"Well, anyway, I'm not going downstairs by myself in the dark," thought Anne. "And I really dare not wake Uncle or Aunt. I must leave Timmy to deal with whatever it is. He can always bark or howl if someone is about!"

Timmy had heard something, and he was sitting in his kennel, ears pricked, a little growl grumbling in his throat. He really didn't dare to bark this time. He had heard something before, when he had barked in George's bedroom, and awakened the whole household – and yet there had been nobody downstairs then that he could see or smell!

But somebody was in the house – someone who had crept in at the kitchen door, when George had left it unlocked! That Somebody had hidden in the coal-cellar, door fast shut, when Timmy had barked and alarmed the household! Now the Somebody was about again, switching

on a small torch, making the little noises that had awakened Anne.

It was Tom, the bad boy of the village! He had been out to a rowdy party, and had passed Kirrin Cottage on his way home. He had tiptoed to the front door, and gone to the garden door and tried both handles – no, they were fast locked! Then he had slipped round to the kitchen door, and to his surprise and delight had found it opening when he turned the handle.

He had crept inside and was just looking round when Timmy had begun to bark upstairs – and quick as a rabbit Tom had slipped into the coal-cellar, and shivered there while the household came out on to the landing, angry with Timmy, who was then put into his kennel.

When all was quiet, and the dog safely in his kennel, the boy looked quietly round to see what he could take. He thought he heard a noise, and stopped in alarm. No, it was only the coals dropping

17

in the grate. He felt scared, and swung his torch round and about to see what he could easily take away with him.

He saw the sack lying by the Christmas tree – how it bulged with the parcels inside it! Tom grinned in delight. 'Must be full of fine presents!' he thought. 'All nicely bundled up in a sack, too – couldn't be easier for me to carry!' He lifted it, put it over his shoulder, and tiptoed out of the kitchen door, shutting it with a little click – the click that Anne had heard from upstairs!

Timmy knew there was someone about, of course – but now he didn't dare to bark. He had been put into his kennel as a punishment for barking – if he barked again and woke Mr. Kirrin, goodness knows what would happen to him! So he kept quite silent, and slipped out of his kennel, and down the garden path after the boy with the sack.

He followed him all the way to the

village, unseen and unheard. How he longed to growl, how he longed to fly at this nasty little robber-boy and nip him sharply in the leg! He saw the boy go through a gate and walk to a shed nearby. He went in, and came out again – but this time without the sack! Then he let himself into the house nearby, shut the door, and disappeared.

Timmy sat down to think. After a minute he went to the shed and slipped through the half-broken wooden door. He smelt the sack at once. That bulging sack belonged to George! Very well – it must at once be taken back to Kirrin Cottage before the boy took out all the presents in it. Timmy sniffed at the parcels inside. His own parcel was there – the one with the bone that Anne had wrapped up for him. Timmy growled. So that boy had DARED to carry away his bone! Timmy decided to take the whole sack back to Kirrin Cottage.

But alas – it was far too heavy for him

to drag out of the shed! What was he to do? He worked his head into the open sack-neck again and pulled out a parcel – then another and another! Good – he would take them one by one to his kennel and hide them there for Christmas morning!

And that is exactly what dear, patient old Timmy did! He took all those parcels one by one to his kennel, trotting back and forth so many times that he began to feel he was walking in a dream! It was lucky that Kirrin Cottage was not far from the boy's home, or he would have been trotting to and fro all night!

At last the sack was empty, and the last parcel safely tucked into the back of his big kennel. There was hardly room for old Timmy to sit in it! Tired out but very happy, he put down his head on his paws, and fell sound asleep.

He was awakened next morning by a great hubbub in Kirrin Cottage! "Aunt Fanny! Uncle Quentin! The sack of presents is gone – and the kitchen door's wide open! Someone's stolen all our presents in the night."

"That's why Timmy barked! He knew there was something going on! Oh, our beautiful presents! What a MEAN trick!"

"But why didn't old Tim catch the thief when he slipped out of the kitchen door with the sack? Poor old Tim – he must have been too scared to do anything, after being scolded for barking before, and made to go to his kennel!"

"Christmas is spoilt!" said Anne, with tears in her eyes. "No presents at all – no surprises – no fun!"

"Woof!" said Timmy, coming out of his kennel, as the four children came up the path. "Woof!"

"Who took our lovely presents, Timmy – and where do you suppose they are now?" said George, sorrowfully. "Didn't you dare to bark, old thing?"

"Woof," said Timmy in an apologetic voice, and went into his kennel. He backed out with something in his mouth – a parcel! He went in and fetched another – and another – and another! He laid them all down in front of the astounded children, wagging his tail.

"TIMMY! Where did you get them? Where's the sack? Did you chase the thief, and take the parcels one by one out of the sack – and bring them home?" asked George, in wonder.

"Woof," said Timmy, agreeing and wagged his tail vigorously. He pawed at one of the parcels, and Anne gave a delighted laugh.

"That's my present to you!" she said. "You knew it was for you, Tim – you smelt the bone inside. Darling, darling Tim, how clever you are! You stored all our presents safely in your kennel, so that we should have them on Christmas morning after all! I'll undo your parcel and you shall have my present first of all!"

"WOOF, WOOF, WOOF!" barked Timmy in delight, and not even Uncle Quentin frowned at the tremendous noise.

"Good old Timmy! Open your parcel and then go indoors and gnaw your bone, while you watch the others open theirs."

Happy Christmas to all the Five – and especially to you, Timmy-dog, especially to you!

Writing
The Famous Five Books

by Enid Blyton's daughter, Gillian Baverstock

Enid Blyton taught herself to type in 1926. She typed faster than most typists, even though she used just two fingers. She said she could easily write 10-12,000 words a day and the reason she did not write more was because her arms became tired.

This helps to explain why it took Enid Blyton only four to five days to write a Famous Five book of approximately 40,000 words in length. When she started the first in the series, 'Five On A Treasure Island', she knew only what type of book she had to write and its length. She put her typewriter on her knees, closed her eyes and waited for the story to come into her imagination.

After a few minutes she saw four children - and soon knew their names and relationships. She was pleased when Timmy appeared because she knew her readers liked animals in their stories.

Gradually the setting grew in her imagination. Kirrin Cottage, the sea and a rowing boat, an island with a castle on the top. She heard the children talking and playing in her head and saw George scowling at the others.

The ideas kept surging up from her imagination and she found it hard to keep up on the typewriter. She said it was like watching a film inside her head and she did not know what was going to happen until she started to write what she saw.

She kept to a daily timetable while writing a book, starting at ten o'clock and stopping for lunch at one o'clock. She would start again about quarter to two and finish writing for the day at half past four. She didn't really like noise and interruptions but when I came home from school

Enid Blyton

I would run in to say 'hello' and grab the pages she had written that day. I read them in my bedroom and at tea-time I would beg her to tell me what happened next, but she never would and I had to wait until the next day.

She had far more to do in a day than just writing. She read over what she had written that day and corrected any proofs of other books that her publishers had sent her. She would check artists' pictures carefully, then carefully pack the pictures up again – and there was no Sellotape in those days, only sealing wax. Then she would have to answer all her letters - at least 50 every

20

day, some business letters and some from children. She answered them all and never used a secretary.

She was the busiest person I have ever known, yet she still had time to read, to talk, to arrange her flowers, to play golf or tennis, or to garden. However, when she was writing a long book she had little time for anything else but she did not mind because for her writing was not work, it was a pleasure.

The Setting For Kirrin

Studland Bay, ...tales told of smugglers.

Corfe Castle which dominates the village.

'Old Harry'.

It was March 1941 and I was eight years old. I had been ill and my mother had taken me away to Swanage in Dorset to get some sea air.

Swanage was the centre of a pretty bay with chalk cliffs to the east, ending where the Old Harry rocks stuck out of the sea, and a rocky wall to the west turning on to chalk cliffs that eventually led to Weymouth. The rough sea round the rocky point had worn away softer layers forming caves, fantastically shaped rocks and strange blow holes. Somewhere near there was a lighthouse that we explored.

Beyond the cliffs lay Studland Bay. There were caves there and tales told of smugglers landing in days gone by.

Not far inland is Corfe with a narrow twisting street and small grey stone houses, all dominated by a tall green mound topped by an old castle with the remains of a tower rising up just off centre. We climbed the mound and found trees growing through stone and I am sure that we heard jackdaws calling 'chack chack' as we sat down.

'Five On A Treasure Island' was published in 1942. In those days a book took a good ten months from leaving the writer's pen and appearing in the shops. That means that my mother probably wrote the book a few months after our holiday in Swanage.

For me, Corfe Castle has always been the image of Kirrin Castle on the island. The fact that Corfe is surrounded by streets and houses and Kirrin Castle was surrounded by sea is immaterial. The whole shoreline of that area of Dorset may very well be the background she saw for that story, especially as we had explored it all just a few months earlier.

21

Nature Zone QUIZ

The Famous Five invite you to go out and about in the countryside! Julian, George, Dick, Anne and Timmy ask the questions and you give the answers!

1 This bird has sometimes appeared in a Famous Five adventure, nesting in old ruined castles. It's a clever bird that can imitate human sounds and talk. Unmix the letters to identify it:

KAWJACD

2 One of the following is not a freshwater fish: Trout, roach, cod, pike. Which is the odd one out?

3 Two wild animals similar in looks are the weasel and the stoat. Which is the larger?

4 Here are three of the most common trees in Britain. Name them by filling in the blanks:

A. P _ PL _ _
B. _ YC _ M _ R _
C. B E _ _ H

5 It's a pleasure to pass by an 'olde-worlde' watermill on a country walk. They were made to help the rivers flow – true or false?

6 Try to finish this well-known country saying: As wise as an _ _ _ ?

7 A rainbow consists of seven colours: Red, orange, yellow, blue, indigo, violet and _ _ _ _ _ ?

8 A cattle grid is constructed of metal bars set in the ground. What is it for:
A. to stop cattle crossing?
B. to stop people crossing?
C. to count the cattle?

9 You've been lucky and spotted a country creature. It hasn't seen you. But there's a wind blowing, which could carry your scent to the animal and scare it off. To avoid this happening, where should you be standing – with the wind blowing at you from the front, or from behind you?

10 Which kind of farm animal has these three different breeds: Guernsey, Jersey, Friesian?

11 The bat is a strange creature in many ways. It flies like a bird, yet is a mammal. But is it right or wrong to say that the bat is the only mammal that can fly?

12 This famous wild flower known as a 'clock' grows in cities as well as the country. Add the missing letters to spell its name: _ A N _ _ L _ O N

13 Conkers is a great game. From which tree do we get conkers: Pine, ash, oak or horse chestnut?

14 Choose from this list to indicate the name of the badger's home: Set, burrow, den, lair?

15 An attractive tree that's often seen growing by rivers. It's called the Weeping _ _ _ _ _ ?

16 Lost your way? There's a wild plant that can help give you directions! Moss grows on the side of trees facing which way: east, west, north or south?

17 Three important things you must do when crossing farmland. Unjumble the words in these sentences:
A. Close any STAGE you open
B. Don't damage any PROCS
C. Don't bother any SMANILA

18 The mole isn't found in one of these countries: Ireland, Wales, Scotland, England. Which one?

19 Like other conifers, the larch tree keeps its leaves in winter – true or false?

20 There are different mice in the countryside. Can you tell which one of these isn't real: dormouse, harvest mouse, grass mouse, wood mouse?

Answers on page 61

BE A TREASURE HUNTER!

Julian tells you how to use your eyes and intelligence to find old things – just like The Famous Five!

Gold, silver, ancient coins! Fancy digging them up? Most of you won't get THAT lucky. But there are plenty of other old relics you might discover. Just look for the right clues...

CLUE: Rubbish!
It was usually just thrown out by our ancestors. No dustbins in those days! The rubbish ended up buried. Perfect pickings for treasure hunters of today.

CLUE: Study old maps of your area, in your local library. Also try your local parish records (often located in the church).

On the maps, you'll see details of villages. Some existing, some that have vanished. The same goes for houses and cottages. You may need permission to go hunting in these places, so check first. Never go alone, go with friends. Ask a parent or trusted adult to accompany you for safety reasons.

Once you start 'grubbing' (with a small trowel) at an old site you've chosen, you'll be surprised at what might turn up.

Most likely finds are pieces of pottery, stoneware or porcelain. Parts of plates and old claypipes are also common – perhaps not of any great value in money terms, but they can make a nice collection for you.

Maybe you'll unearth something made of metal like a candle-holder or gardening tool. A luckier find would be an ancient bottle. Often the shape helps to guess a bottle's age.

CLUE: Before 1800, bottle making wasn't perfected and there were defects in the blowing. As for pottery fragments, the makers often put their 'ceramic marks' on the bottom.

A warning in case you really do dig up gold, silver or ancient coins. You can't just keep them or you risk breaking the law. A find is known as Treasure Trove and generally speaking belongs to the Crown. The discovery must be handed in to a local or national museum. But it's not all bad news. Full compensation in money is paid to the finder, although the find is sometimes returned to him or her instead.

A man digging in his vegetable garden found a dump of old bottles. He was astonished when some of them were valued as being worth many hundreds of pounds. This could happen to you!

These marks can be dated by checking lists in reference books at your local library.

CLUE: More detective work for the serious treasure hunter. To trace where an old house or cottage once stood, look for the following: bushes and plants not normally found growing wild; groups of trees set in a particular pattern; layouts of what was once a garden or orchard.

Other possible sites to visit are old vanished canals, railways and historical battlefields. But never go anywhere that might be a danger.

Your treasure finds could be really ancient. Maybe Roman. There are lots of places in Britain connected with the Romans. Again, check maps in the library.

CLUE: Many long gone Roman buildings like forts were erected on mounds and hills. Such sites might be overgrown with vegetation and not be immediately visible. Search hard!

Further back in time, Bronze Age people made use of flint stone to make arrowheads, axeheads and other working tools. Difficult to find. But if you do – Wow!

CLUE: Look for chipped or 'napped' flints, with a 'tool' shape.

So you see, digging up history is fun. And guess what? Dick, Anne and George (and Timmy, of course) enjoy treasure hunting.

Now I've given you clues of what to do, go to it. This is Julian saying 'get grubbing!'

WALKING IN THE WILDS

Always be prepared, just like The Famous Five!

A day out hiking the countryside! Away from houses, streets and traffic. That's an adventure, you can be sure.

But hold on. Let's plan and prepare a bit first. We don't want to have the fun spoilt when we're off rambling. Take a note of what to do and what not to do when walking in the wilds.

ALWAYS Go in a group of at least four people and never alone. If an accident happens, one of the group stays with the injured person while the other two go for help.

NEVER Go without a trusted adult such as a parent. That's essential, for your own personal safety.

ALWAYS Tell someone you're going on the trek and which route you intend to take.

NEVER Take time for granted. Start early, stop early. Give yourselves plenty of time to make the trip and return home before it gets dark.

SURVIVAL KIT

These items are essential for our day's wild walk:
- Waterproof rucksack
- Map and compass
- Torch (plus spare batteries and bulb)
- Whistle (for signalling)
- Mirror (for signalling)
- Spare socks and sweater
- Pencil and notebook (for making notes of our journey, drawing maps, writing messages)
- First Aid (see next page)

Now let's be on our way. We must stick to footpaths and trails, not go wandering off. Stay together as a group and don't let anyone fall behind. We'll take it in turns to be leader, as leading is more tiring than being a follower. Walk at the speed of the slowest person.

STOP Take a rest every hour. Spend 10 minutes relaxing. Have a drink, a snack and make clothes and boots comfortable again. Check your bearings with a map and compass.

WALKING Walk steadily. No racing along, then suddenly stopping. This is actually more exhausting than a good plodding pace.

UPHILL Take shorter steps. Walk with boots flat on the ground, not on your toes. Zigzag up the hill.

DOWNHILL Zigzag down. Short steps, slow pace. Bend knees and dig in heels. No leaning backwards – you could slip and fall.

ALWAYS Plan your route. Use a guide book and map. Choose interesting places and sights to pass.

NEVER Ignore the weather. Check the forecast in newspapers, TV and radio. Phone the local 'Weathercall' service.

ALWAYS Wear proper clothing and a jacket that's waterproof. Lightweight trekking boots or leather walking boots are good for crossing rough ground. Also hat and gloves in cooler weather.

NEVER Wear trainers. They're too soft and liable to cause foot injuries.

FIRST AID KIT

- First Aid book
- Large and small safety pins
- 2 or 3 triangular bandages
- Crepe bandage
- Different-sized plasters
- Antihistamine cream (for insect bites)
- Antiseptic wipes and cream
- Selection of gauze dressings and pads
- Plastic gloves (for hygiene)
- Corn plasters and foot felt
- Scissors
- 'Space' blanket or plastic sheet

One of the group should have a basic knowledge of first aid. On most hikes, nothing at all happens in the way of accidents you'll be glad to hear.

The most common injuries are foot sores and blisters, cramp, sprained ankles, insect bites or stings. These can be treated by the group's first aid expert.

If there's a more serious accident, the most important thing is to quickly get proper medical help. We mustn't panic but keep calm.

Do not move the injured person as this could make things worse. Reassure the casualty and wrap in a 'space' blanket or plastic sheet.

It's this sort of situation where the group of at least four is vital. One to stay, two to get help. These two should write down in the notebook details of the casualty's position and condition. They should take a map and compass with them for finding directions.

MAP AND COMPASS:

Check every so often. Ask two questions: which way are we going? How far is it to our destination?

To know you're going in the right direction makes everyone feel confident. At least one of the group should understand how to use a map and compass.

What if we lose the compass? Use a watch and the sun! Point the hour hand of the watch at the sun. Now imagine there is a line halfway between the hour hand and twelve o'clock. That imaginary line will point to the south.

What if we get lost? Amazing as it sounds, it's pretty impossible to get lost! What's happened is we've forgotten where we are. So let's stop, check the terrain using map and compass. We'll find our way again.

WATCH OUT FOR:

Wet grass – We'll keep off it. It's very slippery and we might fall over, resulting in an injury.

Tall vegetation – Keep out of grass, bushes, brambles, bracken. There might be unseen holes or rocks which could twist a foot. Or snakes, ants and so on.

Steep slopes – Don't tackle them. Especially downhill slopes where many accidents happen due to our quickening pace.

Water – Steer clear of rivers, streams, ponds, pools, lakes and so on. If anyone has ideas of crossing a stream or river, don't even think about it. Even if the water looks shallow and clear, there could be hidden dangers such as mud, weeds, rocks or other obstacles. Say NO!

Weather – Watch it all the time. It can suddenly change, especially in hilly areas. If caught in a storm, never stand under a tree where lightning could strike. The safest place to stay is on open ground.

Now you are ready for walking SAFELY in the wilds. You know you can handle most problems. Most likely, you won't have any – just a great adventure!

MUNCHING ON THE MOVE

On a day's hike, you don't want to waste good walking time with cooking. Nor have your rucksack weighed down with tins and so on. So, bring along a packed lunch. Sandwiches, bread rolls with cheese spread for example. Fruit such as apples, bananas, oranges. Lunch will be a short break, like half-an-hour.

We can nourish ourselves while on the move. Snacks such as biscuits, crackers, chocolate bars and boiled sweets. They're nice to nibble and good for giving energy.

Take plenty to drink, though. Walking is thirsty work. Without enough liquid, we'd become dehydrated and ill. A flask of hot tea or coffee will help us to keep going.

Good Old Timmy!

"Aren't you ready to come down to the beach and bathe, Anne?' yelled George, standing at the bottom of the stairs. "We're all waiting for you. Do HURRY UP!"

The study door flew open and Mr. Kirrin, George's father, appeared. "Georgina! Will you stop shouting all day long? How can I work? For pity's sake, clear out of the house."

"We're just going, Daddy – and as we're taking a picnic lunch we shan't be disturbing you for some time. I know you're on a big job – it's bad luck it's holiday time and we're here!"

Uncle Quentin grunted and disappeared into his study. Aunt Fanny appeared with two big bags of sandwiches. "Oh dear – was that your Uncle Quentin shouting again?" she said. "Never mind! He doesn't mean to be bad-tempered – but he really is on a big job at the moment, and he's trying to get some figures for the scientist he's working with, a

Professor Humes, who is staying in Kirrin – at the Rollins Hotel. Now – here are your sandwiches – and biscuits and apples – and you can take some bottles of ginger-beer out of the larder."

Just then Anne raced down the stairs, and the Five, all in swimsuits went off to the beach to bathe and laze and play games on the sands. Only three people were there – two men and a lonely looking boy. Julian found a cool cave and put the food on a shelf of rock.

"What about a swim straight away?" he said. "Hello – Timmy's off to rub noses with that dog we saw yesterday – the big ugly brute we didn't much like. He belongs to those two men. They're not much to look at either! I wouldn't like to meet them on a dark night!"

"Well, Timmy seems to like their dog all right," said George, staring at the two dogs sniffing at one another, then tearing along the sands together, barking happily.

"Look," said Dick, "there's that kid coming along the beach again, the one we saw yesterday. Shall we ask him to come bathing with us – he seems to be all on his own. Look out, kid – don't get knocked over by our dog!"

Timmy had come racing up joyfully, chasing the other dog, and the boy went sprawling as they galloped round him. Timmy turned in surprise and saw the boy rolling over and over on the sand. He gave an apologetic bark, and ran to the small boy, licking and sniffing at him.

The boy was terrified of Timmy. He began to scream in terror, and Julian ran to him. "He's only making friends, he's only saying he's sorry he knocked you over, he won't hurt you! Come on, get up – we were just going to ask you to come and bathe with us."

"Oh," said the boy, and stood up, shaking the sand off himself. He looked to be about nine or ten, and small for his age.

"Well, thanks. I'd like to bathe with you. I'm Oliver Humes, and I'm staying at the Rollins Hotel."

"Then your father must be a friend of our uncle," said Dick, "He's called Kirrin – Quentin Kirrin – and he's a scientist. So is your father, isn't he?"

"Yes. A very fine one too," said Oliver proudly. "But he's worried this morning."

"Why? What's up?" said George.

"Well – he's working on something important," said Oliver, "and this morning he had a horrible letter. It said that unless Dad agreed to give the writer information he wanted about what Dad was working on, he'd – he'd kidnap me!"

"Oh rubbish!" said Julian. "Don't you worry about that! We'll tell our dog Timmy to look after you. Just look at him playing with that ugly great mongrel. Timmy's a mongrel too – but we think he's beautiful!"

"I think he's too big," said Oliver,

fearfully, as Timmy came running up, panting. The other dog went back to the two men, who had just whistled for him.

"Come on – let's swim," said Dick.

"I can't swim," said Oliver. "I wish you'd teach me."

"Right. We will when we've had our bathe," said Anne. "We'll go into the water now. Come on!" And soon the Five, Timmy too, were splashing in the sea, yelling and diving in and out, having a glorious time, while Oliver paddled near the shore. Then suddenly Julian gave a shout, and pointed to the beach.

"Look! What's happening there? Hey!" All the Five looked, and saw something very surprising! The two men who owned the big brown dog were dragging Oliver out of the water, one with his hand over the boy's mouth.

"They're kidnapping him! Remember that threatening letter he told us of, that his father had this morning? Come on, quick – see if we can stop them. TIMMY! Come on, now!"

They swam to the shore and slipped hurriedly into their sandals. "They've taken the kid up the cliffs – they're at the top, look!" panted Julian. "After them, Timmy!"

But not even Timmy could get up the cliffs in time to rescue the screaming boy. Julian was at the top first, with Timmy – just in time to see a car driving off. The big dog was galloping after it.

"Why didn't they take the dog in the car, too?" wondered Dick.

"Perhaps he's a car-sick dog?" said Anne. "Anyway, I bet he knows where the men are going, and has been ordered to follow. If the car doesn't go too fast he can easily keep up."

"I've got the number, anyway," said Dick.

"Listen – I think Anne's right when she says the dog must know where the men are going," said Julian. "And it can't be far away if the dog has to run the whole distance."

Timmy was not listening. He was sniffing the ground here and there. Then he suddenly began to trot along the cliff-road, nose to ground. George gave a sudden exclamation.

"I know! He's sniffing the other dog's tracks – he knows his smell, and he's following it!"

"You're right! Look – let's see if he'll follow the trail properly," said Julian. "He might lead us to Oliver! Tell him, George. He always understands every word you say."

"Timmy! Listen!" said George, and pointed to some paw-marks made in the sandy road by the big mongrel dog. "Follow, Timmy, follow. Understand?"

Timmy lifted his big head and looked hard at George, his ears cocked, his head on one side. Yes – he understood. Then, with nose to ground he trotted swiftly away down the cliff-road, sniffing the tracks of the other dog. How did he do it? What a nose he had, old Timmy!

"Come on," said Dick. "Timmy will lead us to wherever those fellows are taking Oliver."

Very steadily, Timmy followed the scent down the cliff-road, turned off to the left, trotted down a lane, swung to the right, then to the left. He waited at the traffic lights, and when they changed to

green, he crossed the road, and then trotted right through the town, nose to trail! The children padded behind in their swimsuits, Anne getting very puffed!

At the other end of the town Timmy turned to the left and padded down a lane, nose still on the scent! The four followed closely. "I shall have to have a rest soon," panted Anne.

"I say, that's the car that took the boy away!" exclaimed Dick, suddenly, as they passed a garage, outside which stood a black car taking in petrol. "The men are in it. But I can't see Oliver – and that great dog isn't anywhere about, either."

"Well, they must have hidden Oliver somewhere not far off, and then they came back here for petrol," said Julian. "Go on, Tim, old fellow – you're on the right trail. I expect they've left that dog in charge of the boy. I bet if anyone went near, he'd tear them to pieces!"

"And I don't want old Timmy in a dog-fight," said George.

"Yes, not so good," said Julian, and came to a stop. Timmy, however, went on, and wouldn't come back, even though George called him.

"Obstinate old thing!" said George crossly. "Once he's following a trail nothing on earth will stop him. Well – I'm going after him in case he gets into trouble!"

"Look – Timmy's gone through that gateway," said Anne, "into a field. There's a shed at the bottom of it. Could Oliver be there, with the dog inside, guarding him?"

Timmy stopped suddenly and began to growl. George ran to catch hold of his collar. But Timmy wrenched himself away and raced to the shed, scraping at the wooden door. Immediately a volley of fierce barks came from the shed. The Five halted.

A voice came from the shed. "Help! Help, I'm locked in here!"

"There – Timmy followed the trail correctly!" said George. "Quick, Jules – we mustn't let him break in that door – the

other dog will fly at him, and at us, too! Whatever can we do?"

It was obvious that the other dog had been left on guard, and would fling himself on anyone or anything that tried to prevent him from doing his duty.

"TIMMY! STOP THROWING YOURSELF AGAINST THAT DOOR!" yelled George. "YOU'LL BREAK IT DOWN, AND THEN GOODNESS KNOWS WHAT WILL HAPPEN!"

As both dogs, barking fiercely, again flung themselves on it from opposite sides, the door cracked in two places – and the bottom half shook and shivered! "Anne, George, quick, come with me!" said Julian. "We may be attacked by that dog once he gets out! Run! We could perhaps climb that tree, look. Buck up, for goodness sake!"

Terrified, the two girls raced for the tree, and the boys shoved them up, clambering on to a branch themselves.

CRASH! The door fell to the ground,

broken in half. At once the great mongrel leapt out. But it took absolutely no notice of Timmy. It ran, instead to the tree and stood below, growling fiercely. Timmy stood staring in surprise. Why was this dog growling at the children? It was all a mistake, Timmy decided, and he must put it right.

He ran to the tree, and whined as if to say: "It's all right. Do come down and play with us!" Then he went to the other dog, and whined to him too.

The mongrel gave a loud bark, and jumped up. He ran off a little, stopped and turned round as if saying to Timmy: "All right – you want a game? Then so do I! You're the dog I played with this morning, aren't you? Well, come on, let's have a game!"

And, to the children's enormous astonishment the two dogs gambolled amiably together!

"I feel a bit silly up here," said Dick,

30

climbing down. "Come on – the war's over. Those dogs look as if they're friends for life. Let's go and get that kid."

With the frightened boy safely in their midst, they began to walk cautiously out of the field. The two dogs took absolutely no notice! The big mongrel had got Timmy down on the ground, and was pretending to worry him. Timmy was having the time of his life!

"Look – there's a bus going to Kirrin!" said Julian, delighted. "Stop it! We'll get in and take Oliver back to safety while we've a chance. Timmy will just have to walk. He'll make that dog forget all about guarding Oliver!"

It was not very long before they were safely back in Kirrin. Oliver looked very white, but when Julian told him solemnly that it was really a Very Big Adventure, he cheered up and began to boast! "I was kidnapped! Coo – what will the boys at school say? But I was jolly scared though.

Can we go and find my father?"

Professor Humes was very thankful to see his son again, for already he had notified the police that he had disappeared. Dick gave the police the number of the men's car. "You'll soon track that all right!" he said. "But not so well as old Tim here – he used his nose, and a jolly good nose it is too!"

"Woof!" said Timmy, and let his tongue hang out of his mouth.

"He says he's hot and thirsty," said George. "Let's buy him an ice-cream."

"We'll ALL have the biggest ice-creams there are in the village shop," said the Professor, patting Timmy. "I could do with one myself."

"I could do with four," said Oliver, "so I hope you're feeling generous, Dad! Dad, you should have seen Timmy following the trail! He's a wonder dog!"

"Well, we've always known that," said George. "Come on, Timmy – ICE-CREAMS!"

Timmy's Tale

by Gillian Baverstock

Enid Blyton loved animals and when I was a little girl we were surrounded by dogs, cats, turtle doves, tortoises, fantail pigeons, hens, turkeys, goldfish and a canary. She bred Siamese cats and fox terriers and as I grew older I had mice and my sister eventually had a horse.

When Enid was a child she was never allowed to have a pet of any sort. Her father wouldn't have one because it would dig up his garden and her mother refused to consider a pet because it would mess up the house. Once Enid found a little lost kitten and brought it home. She called it Chippy and she kept it hidden in a back shed. She looked after it carefully and played with it lovingly after school. One dreadful day, Enid returned from school and found the kitten had gone. Her mother had discovered it and got rid of it immediately.

It was not until she was eighteen that Enid was able to have all the animals she wanted. She went to live with some friends who had a farm while she did her three years teachers' training in the kindergarten at Ipswich Girls High School. During those three years she enjoyed the farm dogs and cats and working on the farm with all the animals. It was during that time that she learned enough about farming to write her books about farms.

Some of the dogs that she had owned appeared in her books. Our spaniel, Laddie, became 'Loonie' in 'The Rockingdown Mystery'; several dogs in different books were very like her beloved fox terrier, Bobs. Bobs was a very clever dog that Enid Blyton trained herself and he could do all sorts of tricks just like Jimmy's dog, Lucky, in 'Mr Galliano's Circus'. He even wrote letters to children in 'Sunny Stories' and 'Teachers' World'.

Timmy is much the most well known and loved dog that Enid Blyton created. I like to imagine that he might have been one of the farm dogs – perhaps the first dog that she was able to love and care for. Enid Blyton said in her autobiography: 'Timmy was a real dog but he did not look quite as he does in the books because the artist had never seen him.'

Perhaps it is a good thing that we don't know what Timmy really looked like because in a film you have to look for a dog who can do everything that Timmy can, but it is impossible to find a dog that looks exactly like his pictures as well. Connal in the TV series is the most loving and loyal dog and he is just like Timmy in all the ways that really matter.

Timmy adores the company of the children.

Timmy keeps an eye on George.

ALARM CALL!

You are facing disaster it seems...

Maybe you're stranded in a remote area, miles from people and civilisation. You've got no radio or it's damaged and not working.

Whatever the difficulties, you need help fast. How do you let rescuers know where you are?

You'll be relieved to discover there are ways! Almost always, rescue services eventually get to have a rough idea of your whereabouts. They'll know more or less in which area to make a search. But the area might be very large and you'll be like the proverbial needle in the haystack.

You can help the rescuers find you! This means making signs and signals of some sort to indicate your position. Besides attracting the attention of rescuers like a helicopter or aircraft, you can also communicate the kind of assistance you need.

Other points to remember:
- The signs should be placed where they can be seen from all directions. A wide open area is best, away from trees and boulders.
- Signs should be very big, so they are visible from above. At least 10 metres by 3 metres.
- A helicopter or aircraft that has spotted you will dip its wings or flash its lights.
- Signs should have simple shapes. Straight lines and square corners to contrast with the terrian.
- All signs must be got rid of after rescue to avoid other rescuers wasting their time.

A BRIGHT IDEA

Signalling with a mirror can be very effective. Using light off the sun, first check it's working by reflecting a flash on the ground.

When the rescue aircraft or helicopter approaches, shine the reflected flash skywards. Mirror signals can reach a long way - up to a distance of 50 miles! If you don't have a mirror, use some other metal object such as a plate or cup.

A torch or a whistle are probably the most familiar for sending signals. You can also do it with your own voice!

The International Distress Signal is six torch flashes, whistle blasts or vocal shouts. One minute of silence. Then repeat the six signals. The answering signal is three flashes, blasts or shouts every minute.

A GOOD POINT

Place stones on the ground in the shape of an arrow. The sign will act as a guide to rescuers searching on land trying to track you down. Point the arrow towards your location. If you're not in a stony area, use sticks instead.

Why not photocopy this page from The Famous Five Annual and take it on your trips!

DANGER SIGNS

The signs here are internationally recognised. They are known by rescue services all over the world. So no matter which country you're in, you won't have to worry about the local language. These international symbols will do the job.

Send food and water	F
Send map and compass	O
Need signal lamp or radio	¦
Serious injuries, send doctor	I
Send medical supplies	II
Show direction to proceed	K
Am going in this direction	↑
Unable to proceed	X
Probably safe to land here	△
Need fuel and oil	L
Aircraft badly damaged	⊏
Need engineer	W
Will attempt take-off	▷
Yes	Y
No	N
Not understood	⌐L
All is well	LL

The signs can be set up with sticks, stones or lengths of rags. Also marked in snow, sand, dust or dirt.

GET THE MESSAGE

Normally transmitted by radio, the Morse Code can also be sent by torch flashes or whistle blasts.

A ·—	M — —	Y —·— —
B —···	N —·	Z — —··
C —·—·	O — — —	1 ·— — — —
D —··	P ·— —·	2 ··— — —
E ·	Q — —·—	3 ···— —
F ··—·	R ·—·	4 ····—
G — —·	S ···	5 ·····
H ····	T —	6 —····
I ··	U ··—	7 — —···
J ·— — —	V ···—	8 — — —··
K —·—	W ·— —	9 — — — —·
L ·—··	X —··—	0 — — — — —

AAAAAA means: I am sending a message.
R means: Message received.

A Heap Of Old Rubble?
THINK AGAIN!

Toppled towers, broken walls, collapsed archways. We all enjoy seeing a good old fashioned ruin. There's so much mystery about them. The gloomy atmosphere grips you. Luckily for us, Britain is littered with ruins so you could spend years touring them.

Neglect is not the only cause of buildings being abandoned. Some were destroyed in time of war.

Corfe Castle in Dorset is such a victim. It was devastated in 1648, during the English Civil War. The castle's owners supported King Charles and Cromwell's army took revenge by attacking it. Gunpowder charges were placed to smash the walls. But Corfe Castle was strong and well built and the walls didn't fall. Instead they were pushed out at an angle. You can see this today.

One of the towers survived in an amazing way. Cromwell's soldiers had dug a hole underneath, set in the gunpowder and detonated it. But the tower wasn't blown up. It just sank straight down into the hole and even now still stands on two levels. It makes a great picture for your photo collection!

Some ruins are romantic, like Valle Crucis Abbey in the Vale of Llangollen, North Wales. These remains are popular because of their spectacular 'good looks', located in beautiful hilly scenery. The abbey is 'most pleasantly decayed' said one historian. No wonder it attracts lots of tourists!

There are other ruins that have *always* been ruins. During the 17th century, a grand new house, Lyveden New Bield, was being built in Northamptonshire. But the wealthy owner, Sir Thomas Tresham, made the mistake of getting mixed up in the Gunpowder Plot against King James the First. Tresham was punished and the construction of the house stopped.

Hundreds of years later, the ruin is still there. It sounds just the kind of scary place where a Famous Five adventure might start!

Probably Britain's most famous ruin is Stonehenge. It's certainly one of our oldest, going

Try visiting the ruins in your own area. At first, some of them might seem just piles of old rubble. But give them a chance and you'll become fascinated by their mystery. You may need to get permission first before visiting. Please go with care and take a trusted adult along with you. Check if an admission fee is charged.

One of The Famous Five's greatest adventures happens among the ruins of an old castle. The book is called 'Five On A Treasure Island'. The thrills are non-stop!

back 3,000 years!

Stonehenge, in Wiltshire, remained a massive mystery until relatively recently. Everyone was baffled as to how old it was and what it was doing there.

Incredibly, those huge old stones are reckoned to be something like a primitive computer! The people who erected Stonehenge so long ago used it to worship the sun. Clever in mathematics, they positioned the stones so they could track the path of the sun. They worked out

exactly the time and place where the sun rises and sets every day.

Archaeologists and scientists can't understand how the people of Stonhenge did it, but they could also predict the next eclipse of the sun, even if it wasn't due for years.

Visit Stonehenge and you'll be impressed when you think about it.

Creepy, crumbly old ruins – they're magic. They give you a sense of being transported back in time. We love them and we bet you will, too!

Timmy explains...

How To Train Your Dog!

You'd like to have a dog as nice as me, wouldn't you? You know, with all my fine qualities
– being clever, brave, loyal, talented (er ... that's enough self-praise, Timmy – George).
Woof – sorry, got a bit carried away there. Anyway, here are some really good tips
on how to train your dog the right way. All you need to use are four basic command words:

Come Put a long lead on your dog. Walk a short distance away. Then call 'Come' as you gently pull on the lead. Practise the call, moving further away each time. Later, do it without the lead.

Stay Walk a little way off from your dog and call 'Stay'. When the dog stays, pat and praise. Walk back further and repeat the call. Keep doing this until your dog understands it must stay when you're a long distance away.

Sit Giving the call 'Sit', push your hand down on to the dog's back to get into a sitting position. Be gentle, no hard shoving.

Down Use both hands on shoulders and back to press your dog to lie down. Call 'Down' as you do so.

Teach Yourself...

You might need some training! So here are some rules for yourself. Be patient and kind. Be nice when teaching your dog the four command words. Never get cross. Us dogs have feelings, you know!

ALWAYS use exactly the same words for each call.
NEVER change them. One word is best. More than one can confuse. Example: if you call 'Sit down', the dog will wonder what you mean – 'sit' down or 'lie down'. We can't get it right if you don't say it correctly!

Two lessons a day of five minutes each is enough. Longer than that will bore you as well as the dog. Training will take many days. So, remember, lots of patience!

Puppies are easiest to train, although very young puppies, up to the age of four months, are impossible to teach anything. Just leave them to play until they're more grown. An older dog needs more time.

Naughty But Nice...

Plenty of praise and easy on the punishment, please! We like to make you happy, be friends with you. So no hitting or getting angry.

If you don't like something, tell us and just say 'no'. Tell us at the time of being naughty, not later when we've forgotten what we're supposed to have done wrong!

Rewards are nice! We love being patted and stroked, played games with and made a fuss of. Who doesn't? Dog biscuits are very welcome!

Last of all, don't make training your dog too serious. It's not meant to be a test.

Life with your dog should be about being happy together. Like George and me, be the greatest of pals. Woof! Woof!

If a dog *is* naughty, it won't usually be the dog's fault. It'll be the owner's! Be good with your dog and the dog will be good. If you're not so nice, nor will the dog be!

A new puppy in your home needs its own bed. You can buy one or use a box with an old cushion or blanket.

Your puppy might be too nervous to sleep the first few nights. A ticking clock in the bed will help it to nod off!

Tails To Tell

Rescue Dog...

Billy the bull-terrier loved his life with a circus lion tamer. But one performance in Düsseldorf, Germany, went wrong.

The lion tamer was knocked down by a lioness. His leg broken, he couldn't move and the lioness was about to attack again.

There were two attendants for such an emergency – but they panicked and ran for it. Billy to the rescue!

The little bull-terrier sped through the gate left open by the attendants. Barking and growling and snarling, he chased the lioness back.

And so his friend the lion tamer was saved. Billy was the hero of the circus. Shake a paw on it, Billy!

Action Dog...

You can always trust a labrador – and here's a true story to prove it!

A little English girl called Joan was playing in the garden, watched over by the family labrador Tommy. But young Joan got curious about the garden gate, opened it and toddled out – into the middle of the road!

A car was coming too fast to stop! But the quick action labrador was already there. Grabbing the little girl's dress with his teeth, he dragged her out of the way just in time.

Little Joan's parents always knew their labrador was bright. Now they called him a genius!

Twenty tail-wags to you, Tommy!

Dogs like this young Weimaraner need plenty of training!

Danger Dog...

Another wonder-woof-ul story about a labrador is this one. Talk about trekking skills!

Along with another dog and a cat, the labrador found himself 300 miles from home in Canada. This had happened because their owner had placed them with other people while he was away. But the labrador missed his home. So off he went, followed by the others, to find the way back.

Thick forests, wild rivers, dangerous mountains. The three friends crossed them all. And they made it!

Weeks later, the labrador and his pals arrived home to the shock of their owner.

I think I could sometimes do with that labrador's help on a Famous Five adventure!

GEORGE'S STORY

by Gillian Baverstock

Enid's mother was very fond of her two sons and expected Enid to help in the house and in the kitchen, as well as look after the boys. Enid hated this and tried to get out of domestic work whenever she could. Her father often helped her to escape by saying he wanted her in the garden.

Enid Blyton's mother had been the daughter of a farmer and she believed that it was very important that a girl grew up knowing how to run a house, cook and clean. The boys had to chop wood, bring in the coal and clean shoes, but then they had the freedom to run off to play and go where they wanted. Enid would have loved to have been able to do the same.

Many years after 'Five On A Treasure Island' was written Enid told a friend that George was based on herself. I don't think that she began the book thinking that she would write about herself, she did not write like that. As the book progressed she probably recognised her own feelings as a child, longing to have the same freedom that her brothers had and realised that her imagination had used her own perhaps forgotten feelings when George's personality emerged.

Enid Blyton did not look like George when she was young. She had thick dark brown hair that she wore in plaits and she had brown eyes. She had some of the same characteristics that George had – she was very hot-tempered, so her brothers and friends said, and was also very loyal.

One interesting thing that I noticed while reading the complete Famous Five series is that although all the children grow up through the twenty-one books and change quite considerably, especially Anne, George does not seem to change at all.

When Enid Blyton was in her teens, she was busy at school with sport, work, and music while at home she was trying to become a writer and sending stories and poems away to publishers. She also had several very close friends. I wondered if George did not change in the books because she was only the child Enid but not the teenage Enid. So George, like Peter Pan, could not grow up either.

E nid Blyton was born in South London on 11th August, 1897, in a flat above a shop. She was the eldest of three children and her two brothers were called Hanley and Carey. They moved to Beckenham to a house with a garden and not far from the countryside.

Enid and her father always got on very well and enjoyed doing things together. They would go out for long walks in the country or garden at home. Enid's father was a naturalist and knew an enormous amount about wildlife which he passed on to his daughter when he saw how interested she was. Enid loved books and by the time she was ten, her father let her borrow any of his books that she wanted.

Five Have A Puzzling Time

It was dark and very quiet in Kirrin Cottage – almost midnight. The five were all in bed – yes, Timmy, the dog, too, for he was lying on George's feet, his usual place at night. He was not having a very comfortable time, because George, whose real name was Georgina, was so restless.

She tossed and turned and groaned – and at last awoke Anne, who was in bed next to her.

"What's the matter, George, old thing?" said Anne, sleepily. "Is your tooth aching again?"

"Yes, the brute!" said George, sitting up with her hand to her cheek. "Get off my feet, Timmy, I'll just have to get up and walk about!"

"Poor old George," said Anne. "Good thing you're going to the dentist tomorrow!"

"Don't remind me of that!" said

George, walking up and down the bedroom. "Go to sleep, Anne – I didn't mean to disturb you."

The big clock in the hall downstairs struck twelve, very slowly and solemnly. Anne listened, then her eyes shut and she fell asleep again. George went to the window and looked out over Kirrin Bay, holding a hand to her painful cheek. Timmy jumped off the bed and stood beside her, paws on the window-sill. He knew that George was in pain, and he was troubled. He rested his head against her hand and gave it a tiny lick.

"Dear Timmy," said George. "I hope you'll never have toothache! You'd go mad! Look at Kirrin Bay – isn't it lovely? And you can just see Kirrin Island – my island, Timmy – looming up in the darkness!"

Suddenly George stiffened and frowned. She stared across the bay, and

39

then turned and called urgently to Anne.

"Anne! Quick, wake up! ANNE! Come and see! There's a light shining out on Kirrin Island, a light, I tell you! Somebody's there – on MY island! Anne, come and see!"

Anne sat up sleepily. "What's the matter, George? What did you say?"

"I said there's a light on Kirrin Island! Somebody must be there – without permission too! I shall get my boat and row out at once!" George was very angry indeed, and Timmy gave a little growl. He would most certainly deal with whoever it was on the island!

"Oh, George – don't be an ass!" said Anne. "As if you could get your boat and row across the bay in the middle of the night! You must be mistaken!" She jumped out of bed and went to the window. "Where's this light?"

"It's gone – it went out just as you jumped out of bed," said George. "Who can be there, Anne? I'll wake the boys and tell them. We'll get my boat."

She went quickly down to the room where Dick and Julian lay asleep and shook them roughly.

"Wake up! Oh, DO wake up! Something's going on over in Kirrin Island. I saw a light there. WAKE UP, Julian."

George's excited voice not only woke up the boys, but her father as well. He sat up in bed in the next room, thinking there must be burglars in the house!

"Robbers, my dear!" he hissed in his wife's ear, making her start up in fright. "Where's my big stick?"

"Quentin, it's only the children!" said his wife, sleepily. "I expect George's toothache is worse. I'll go and see."

Everybody met in the boys' room. "What on earth is all this about?" demanded George's father.

"There's a light on Kirrin Island," said George, quite fiercely. "On my island! I'm going to see who it is – and so is Timmy. If no one will come with me I shall go alone."

"Indeed you won't go," said her father, raising his voice angrily. "Get back to bed! Rowing to Kirrin Island in the middle of the night! You must be mad. There can't be anyone there. You've had a bad dream, or something."

"Father, there's a light there – I saw

it!" said George, in a voice as loud as her father's. He went at once to the window and looked out.

"Rubbish!" he said. "Not a glimmer of any sort to be seen! You dreamt it!"

"I did NOT!" said George, angrily. "Somebody is there, I tell you. Trespassing!"

"Well, let them trepass!" said her father. "You and the boys can go over tomorrow."

"I can't!" almost wailed George. "I've got to go to the dentist, and have this beastly, horrible, frightful tooth out. I must go tonight!"

"Shut up, George," said Julian. "Be sensible. Whoever is there will still be there tomorrow. I'll go over with Dick. Anyway, there's no light there now – you probably made a mistake. Go to bed, for goodness sake."

George flung out of the boys' room, and went to her own, furious. Timmy went with her, licking her now and again. Why couldn't he and George go off together, this very minute? Timmy was quite ready to!

40

"Now my tooth's aching worse than ever!" said poor George, angry and miserable, dumping herself violently on her bed. Her mother came over to her with a glass of water and two small pills.

"Take these, George," she said. "Your tooth will soon stop aching. Do be sensible, dear."

"That's one thing old George can't be!" said Anne. "Cheer up, George – that tooth will be gone tomorrow – and there won't be anyone on your island, you'll see – and everything will be right again."

George grunted, and lay down with her aching cheek on her hand. She meant to slip out of bed, and go down to her boat as soon as ever the house was quiet again. But the little pills quickly did their work, and in five minutes her tooth had stopped aching, and she was fast asleep.

In the morning when she awoke, she remembered at once what she had seen the night before – a light on her island! And then she remembered the dentist – oh dear, two perfectly horrible thoughts – someone trespassing on her precious island – and a

tooth to come out! She sat up in bed.

"Anne! My tooth has stopped aching. I shan't go to the dentist, I shall go to Kirrin Island with Timmy and the boys."

But her father thought differently, and after a really furious battle between the hot-tempered George and her equally hot-tempered father, George was packed off with her mother in the car, for her visit to the dentist! Timmy went with her, quite alarmed at all the goings-on!

"Poor old George," said Anne, as the car went off down the road. "She does get so het-up about things."

"Well, anyone gets upset with toothache," said Julian. He stared out over Kirrin Bay, which was as blue as cornflowers that morning. "I wonder if old George did see a light on the island last night? You didn't see one, did you, Anne, when you awoke?"

"No. It was all dark there," said Anne. "Honestly, I think George must have dreamt it! Anyway she can take out her boat this afternoon, and we'll go with her, and have a good look round – that should satisfy her!"

"She may not feel like doing anything except having a bit of a rest," said Dick. "She's had toothache for days now, and it does get you down. I tell you what – we three will get the boat and go over to the island this morning – then, when we find nothing and nobody there – except the rabbits and the jackdaws – we can tell George, and she won't worry any more!"

"Right!" said Julian. "Let's go now, straight away! Uncle Quentin will be glad to be rid of us – he's working hard this morning on one of his newest problems."

George's father was glad to hear that the three were going off for the morning. "Now I shall have the house to myself," he said, thankfully. "Except for Joanna the cook, of course. I hope she doesn't take it into her head to clean out the boiler this morning – I MUST have peace and quiet."

"You ought to invent a boiler that cleans itself out with hardly a whisper!" said Anne, smiling at her uncle. "Anyway, we'll be out of your, way. We're just going!"

They went to the beach, to get

George's boat. There it was, ready waiting! Julian looked across to where Kirrin Island lay peacefully in the sun. He was quite certain there was nobody there! George must have dreamt the light she had seen shining in the night.

"We'll row right round the island and see if there is a boat tied up anywhere, or beached," said Dick, taking the oars. "If there isn't, we'll known there's no one there. It's too far for anyone to swim to. Well – here we go!"

And away they went in the warm spring sunshine, the little waves lapping cheerfully round the boat. Anne leaned back and let her hand dabble in the water – what fun to go over to the island and see all the rabbits – there would be young ones there too, now.

"Here we are, almost at the island," said Julian. "In and out of the rocks we go! My word, I'm sorry for anyone who tries to come here in the middle of the night, unable to see what rocks to avoid! Not a sign of a boat anywhere – George must have dreamt it all!"

Dick rowed the boat carefully between the rocks that guarded the island. "We'll land at our usual little cove," he said. "I bet no one else would know how to get there if they didn't already know the way!"

A low wall of sharp rocks came into sight and Dick rounded it neatly. Now they could see the cove where they meant to land – a little natural harbour, with a calm inlet of water running up to a smooth stretch of sand.

"The water's like glass here," said Anne. "I can see the bottom of the cove." She leapt out and helped the boys to pull in the boat.

"Look at the rabbits!" said Dick, as they walked up the smooth sandy beach. "Tame as ever!"

A small baby rabbit came lolloping up to Anne. "You dear little thing!" she said, trying to pick it up. "You're just like a toy bunny!" But the tiny creature lolloped away again.

"Good thing Timmy's not here," said Julian. "He always looks so miserable when he sees the rabbits, because he knows he mustn't chase them!"

They came to the old ruined castle that had been built long ago on the island. The ancient, broken-down entrance led into a great yard, overgrown with weeds. Now the jackdaws came down from the tower, and chacked loudly round them in a most friendly manner. Some of them flew down to the children's feet, and walked about as tame as hens in a poultry yard.

"Well – it doesn't look as if anyone is here," said Julian, staring round and about.

"And there was no boat anywhere," said Anne. "So how could anyone have come here? Let's see if there are any signs of a fire having been lighted. The flames would be seen at night, if so."

They began to hunt all around. They went in and out of the old castle, examining the floors – but there was no sign of anyone having made a fire.

"If George saw a light, then there must be a lamp or lantern somewhere," said Dick. "Anne, did she see the light high up on the island – as if it came from the tower?"

"She didn't say," said Anne. "But I should think it must have been high up.

We'll go up the old broken-down tower steps as far as we can, shall we? We might see something there – perhaps a lantern. It's possible, I suppose, that someone might have been signalling for some reason!"

But, no matter how they searched, the three could find nothing to explain the light that George had said she saw.

"Let's go and lie down on the grass, and watch the rabbits," said Anne. "Hello – why did the jackdaws all fly up then – and why are they chacking so? What frightened them?"

"Funny!" said Julian, staring at the big black birds, circling round and round above them, calling 'chack-chack-chack' so excitedly. "We didn't scare them, I'm sure. I suppose there can't be someone else here?"

"Well – we'll walk round the island and examine the rocks sticking up here and there," said Dick, puzzled about the jackdaws, too. "Someone might be hiding behind one of them."

"I'm going to take off my sandals," said Anne. "I love running on the smooth sand in bare feet. I shall have a paddle, too – the water's quite warm today!"

The boys wandered off round the island. Anne sat down and undid her sandals. She set them by a big stone, so that she could easily find them again, and ran down to the sea. Little waves were splashing over the smooth golden sand, and Anne ran into them, curling up her toes in pleasure.

"It is really almost warm enough to bathe," she thought. "What a lovely little island this is – and how lucky George is to own it. I wish I had an island belonging to my family, that I could call my own. If I had, I suppose I'd worry, too, like George, if I thought anyone was trespassing here – scaring the rabbits – and even perhaps snaring them!"

Soon Julian and Dick came back together, having gone all round the island, and looked into every cranny. They called to Anne.

"Hello, paddler! Is the water nice and warm? We ought to have brought our bathing suits."

"Perhaps a rabbit took one?" suggested Dick, with a grin. "Or a jackdaw – they're jolly mischievous birds, you know!"

"A jackdaw surely couldn't pick up a sandal!" said Anne. "It would be too heavy. And I simply can't imagine a rabbit running off with one!"

"Well – it's not there," said Dick, thinking to himself that Anne must have been mistaken about putting them both by the big stone. He hunted round, but could not see the other one anywhere – strange! However – there certainly was no one on the island – and, if there had been, someone would certainly not have been so silly as to risk being discovered by stealing one little sandal, in full view of Anne!

"We'll have to leave your sandal, wherever it is, Anne," said Julian, at last. "We ought to get back. Well – the only thing we can tell George is that we saw no one at all here – but that one sandal mysteriously disappeared!"

"Blow!" said Anne, not bothering to put on her one sandal. "Now I'll have to spend some of my precious pocket-money to buy a pair of new sandals. Blow, blow, blow!"

"Come on," said Dick, going down towards their boat. "George will have a blue fit if we don't turn up soon. She'll think that the owner of the mysterious light has caught us and made us prisoners! Buck up, Anne."

They were soon all in the boat again, and the boys took it in turn to row back. Through the crowd of rocks they went, threading their way carefully, and at last came to their own beach. George was there, waiting for them, Timmy beside her!

"You went without me!" she scolded. "You are beasts! What did you find?"

"Nothing and no one. The island is absolutely empty except for its usual inhabitants – rabbits and jackdaws!" said Julian, dragging the boat up the sand. "Your strange light in the night must have been a dream, George, old thing!"

"It was NOT!" said George, and her voice was so angry that Timmy began to bark. "You don't know where to look! Now if Timmy had been with you, he'd have smelt out anyone there – he'd have found

"We haven't seen a sign of a single soul," said Dick. "Better go home again. George may be back by now – wanting to tell us about her tooth, and what she has been through. Poor George!"

"I'll put on my sandals," said Anne, drying her feet by scrabbling them in the warm sand. She ran to the big stone by which she had put them. She stopped – and stared in surprise.

"What has happened to one of my sandals? Dick – Jules – have you taken one? Where have you put it?"

"Sandals? No – we didn't even know where you'd put them," said Julian. "There's one of them there, look – the other must be somewhere near."

But it wasn't. No matter how they all looked, only one of Anne's sandals could be found!

"Well! How silly!" said Anne, amazed. "I know I put them both together, just here. I know I did! Anyway, there's no one to take one of my sandals – and even if there were, why take one, and not both?"

the lamp or lantern – he'd have …"

"All right, all right – but we didn't have Timmy!" said Dick.

"How's the tooth, George?" said Anne, seeing that George's cheek was still swollen. "Did you have it out? Did it hurt?"

But George didn't want to waste time in talking about her tooth.

"It's out," she said, shortly. "Blow the tooth! If I hadn't had to go to the dentist, I could have gone with you – and I BET Timmy and I would have found something, I just BET we would!"

"All right – go there, then – and take Tim with you," said Dick, exasperated.

"That's just what I will do!" said George with a scowl. "We'll soon find out who's hiding there. I shall go this very afternoon – with Timmy. You can come, too, if you like, of course – but I can't see that you will be much use!"

"Oh, we'll come all right!" said Dick. "Even if it's only to say, 'Sucks to you' when you can't find more than we did!"

George had quite made up her mind to go off in her boat after she had had her dinner.

"Though my mouth is so sore I'm sure I shan't be able to eat anything!" she said. However, she ate as much as any of the others! Timmy sat very close to her, sad that she was cross and upset.

It was not a very happy meal. Uncle Quentin was quiet and moody, for his work had not gone well that morning. Aunt Fanny looked worried. George sulked. Timmy kept giving heavy sighs.

Even Joanna the cook added a few cross words as she cleared away the dinner.

"I should like to know who's been at the grapes and oranges," she said. "Someone came downstairs in the night and helped themselves. And Miss George – what did you do with the bag of dog-biscuits that came from the grocer's? I couldn't find any for Tim's dinner."

"Oh don't bother so, Joanna!" said George. "You know where I always put them – in the outhouse, with the chicken-food."

"Well, you didn't this time," said Joanna, huffily.

"You can't have looked," said George. "Oh dear – why do all these things have to happen when I've a bad

tooth?"

"Well – you certainly shouldn't have a bad tooth now,' remarked Julian. 'I thought the dentist …"

"All right, all right – yes, he did pull it out, but it still feels as if it's there," said George, crossly.

"You'd better have a lie-down this afternoon, George," said her mother. "A little sleep will …"

"Put you right!" chorused Julian, Dick and Anne, who had heard this saying of their aunt's a hundred times.

She laughed. "Well – what with toothache all night, and little sleep, it's no wonder poor old George is cross."

"I am NOT cross!" roared George, furiously, and that made everyone laugh, of course. Julian gave her a clap on the back.

"Cheer up, old thing. We'll all go and hunt over the island again this afternoon – and I expect you'll find a couple of pirates, two or three robbers, a ship-wrecked sailor, a …"

George gave a sudden grin. "Shut up, you ass. Don't take any notice of me for a bit. I'll be all right soon."

And she was. She took herself in hand, helped Joanna with the washing-up, and then went to look for the biscuits for Timmy. Sure enough, they were missing, as Joanna had said.

"Blow! I'm sure I put them in the outhouse here," said George, looking all around. "I suppose I couldn't have. What have I done with them? Poor old Tim – you'll have to make do with scraps, I'm afraid, till the butcher boy comes with your meat this afternoon. And by the way, Joanna, I did NOT come down last night and take grapes and oranges. My tooth was much too bad. And I'd like to know something now. Who's been at my big box of chocolates?"

She had opened a large box, and was staring inside. "There's more than half gone!" she said. "Timmy – have you been at them? Were you so hungry, poor fellow?"

"Well, I must say that if he took them he was clever to put back the lid!" said Joanna. "Maybe you ate an orange or two as well, Timmy-dog?"

"Woof," said Timmy, in disgust, and turned his back on Joanna. As if he would steal chocolates or oranges!

George went off to find her mother. "Mother – I feel better now. The swelling in my mouth is going down at top speed. I'll be all right to take the boat out with the others, really I will."

"Well – your father does want peace and quiet this afternoon," said her mother. "Go along, then – and don't get over-tired – you had quite a bad time this morning."

Within ten minutes all the Five were in the boat once more. George looked quite herself again, and Julian grinned at her.

"Well? All set to find what we couldn't find? I must admit that with Timmy to help us, we're much more likely to be successful!"

They soon came to the island. George circled it deftly in the boat, being anxious herself to see that no one had hidden a boat anywhere. She pointed to where a great mass of brown seaweed had piled up on the west shore.

"See what the wind did when we had that terrific gale on Tuesday – brought in masses of seaweed again! Now we'll have an awful smell when it dries out! Hello – what's wrong with the jackdaws, all of a sudden? They're never scared of us! Why are they flying up in such a hurry? There is someone on the island!"

"That's what we thought this morning," said Dick, with a grin. "But there wasn't! Plenty of rabbits, though – hundreds. Thank goodness there's one place left where they can live in peace!"

George swung the boat round and ran it deftly into the little cove. Out they all leapt, and pulled in the boat. Timmy jumped out first and tore up the beach at full speed, barking.

"That'll scare the life out of anyone hiding!" said George, pleased. "Go on, Tim – bark. Hunt around! Sniff everywhere!"

The rabbits scattered at once when they heard Timmy. "Don't you dare to touch them!" George called to him, knowing how much he longed to catch one. "Heel, now, Timmy, heel! I want you to come round every corner of the island with me."

Timmy ran to heel, his long tail swinging happily. He loved Kirrin Island. George set off, meaning to examine every well-loved corner, every possible hiding-place. They came to a group of bushes and

Timmy began to sniff about at once.

"He can smell something there!"said George, excited. "What is it, Tim?"

But apparently he found nothing of interest, and soon joined them again. Then Anne's sharp eyes caught sight of something bright under a bush and she bent down to see what is was. She looked round at the others, astonished.

"Look – orange peel! Someone must have been here then! We would never leave orange peel about! And I say, what's this!"

They all clustered round and looked where Anne was pointing. George bent down and picked up something very small.

"See – a pip – a pip from a grape. Does that ring a bell, anyone?"

"Yes!"said Dick. "Joanna said we'd been at the oranges and grapes – do you suppose that ..."

"No! Who's going to steal a bit of fruit and take it over to the island to eat!" said Julian. "That's too far-fetched, honestly! Let's be sensible!"

"What's Timmy doing?" said Anne,

48

suddenly. "Hey, Tim – don't scrape all the sand off the island!"

Timmy was feverishly scraping at the sand nearby with his front paws. He gave an excited little bark, that sounded pleased. What in the world had he found? The others ran to him at once.

Timmy had made a hole – and in it something showed – it seemed like a bulky bag of some kind. Timmy took hold of it with his teeth, and pulled. It split at once – and to everyone's enormous astonishment, out came a mass of dog biscuits!

How they stared! DOG biscuits! Surely, surely they couldn't be the biscuits that George had bought for Timmy the day before, and put in the outhouse?

"They are!" said George. "Look – exactly the same kind. I say – isn't this peculiar! Who in the world would want to steal dog biscuits and bring them here – and oranges and grapes – and for goodness sake, WHY?"

Nobody could think of an answer. Timmy began to crunch up the biscuits, looking very pleased indeed with himself.

He didn't know who had buried them on Kirrin Island, but he thought it was a very good idea!

"Well, that settles it," said Julian. "You were perfectly right, George – someone is here – and you did see a light on the island in the middle of the night. But how did they get here without a boat?"

"We'll soon find out!" said George grimly. "We know he's a thief, anyhow! Tim – go to it! Find him, find him, whoever he is! Smell him out, Tim, smell him out!"

And off went Tim at once, nose to the ground, following the scent of the thief – now WHERE would he lead them? And whoever would he find? It really was too exciting for words.

Timmy went off at such a speed that the four couldn't keep up with him. He raced off round the castle, nose to the ground, barking loudly.

"He'll certainly warn anyone in hiding that he's on their track," panted Dick. "Where in the world can they be? We've hunted everywhere!"

Over the sand and on to the rocks went Timmy, right up to where the seaweed was piled in great masses by the wind and the waves. He stopped and began to sniff anxiously.

"He's lost the trail!" said George, disappointed. "It's the smell of the seaweed that has put him off."

"Or else whoever was here came in a boat at high tide, which would bring it to the shore – and has sailed off again now the tide has gone out," said Julian, frowning. "There wouldn't be any trail to smell, then. Honestly, there doesn't seem to be anyone hiding – and now that even Tim is stumped, I feel we're too late to find whoever it was."

"Timmy – sniff round again," said George. "Go on – you may pick up some other trail."

Timmy obediently sniffed here and there, and occasionally gave a curious growl of anger. Why? George was puzzled.

"Why does he sound so fierce?" she said. "Really angry! What is it, Timmy, old thing?"

"Perhaps he doesn't like the smell of whoever has been here," said Anne. "Let's sit down for a bit and watch the rabbits and jackdaws. Jules, did you bring any biscuits? I brought some barley sugars, and Dick's brought some chocolate in his pocket – I hope it won't be melted!"

George wanted to go on hunting, but the others felt that it was no use. If Timmy had found the scent, and couldn't follow it, no one else would be able to! Anyway, probably the trespasser was far away by now, safely in his boat!

Anne chose a sunny corner by an old ruined wall, and they sat down. At first the rabbits kept away from the children and Timmy – but soon they came out again, as tame as ever. The jackdaws came down too, running almost up to the children, hoping for a titbit.

Suddenly one jackdaw ran at a baby rabbit and gave it a hard peck in the back of the neck. The tiny thing fell over dazed and all the jackdaws came round it in excitement.

"Oh, they'll all peck it now!" cried Anne, jumping up, "Shoo, you birds!"

The birds flew off, chacking loudly, and the little rabbit began to crawl away, still dazed. It tried to run when the children went after it to pick it up, and disappeared under a bush.

"We'll have to get it out to make sure it's not really hurt," said Anne, anxiously.

So the boys crawled under the bush, trying to find where the tiny creature had hidden itself. As it was a gorse bush it was very prickly, and Dick groaned.

"I'm being torn to pieces by these thorns. The rabbit's gone, Anne. I think it's found a rabbit-hole and gone down it. I expect its mother's down there. She'll lick it better."

They went back to where they had left their biscuits and bars of chocolate. Anne stopped suddenly and stared down in amazement.

"Look! Half the biscuits have gone – and two of the chocolate bars! Surely the jackdaws couldn't have taken them so quickly!"

"There's a broken biscuit over here, look – it must have been dropped by whoever stole them!" said Dick, amazed. "I

say – what sauce to come right to where we were sitting, and take the things just when our backs were turned. I didn't hear a thing!"

"Nor did Tim – or he would have barked," said George, really puzzled. "Whoever it was must have come up as quietly as a mouse!"

"Let Timmy sniff round – he'll pick up the thing's trail," said Julian. "It will be so fresh!"

Timmy was already sniffing, looking very puzzled indeed. The trail didn't seem much use to him! He ran a little way, nose to ground, following it – and then stopped, as if the trail had come to an end!

"Look, Timmy – trails don't finish all of a sudden!" said George, exasperated. "People don't take off in mid-air!"

"There's a tree nearby," said Anne. "Do you think whoever it was could have climbed up into it?"

"Anne, dear – there is NOBODY up the tree," said George, in a patient, what-an-ass-you-are sort of voice. "I've looked."

"Well, let's hunt round a bit again," said Julian, more puzzled than ever. "I

51

know – we'll leave some biscuits and the bag of barley sugars here, and go behind that big gorse bush and hide – and maybe the thief, whoever he is, will come along and take those. He seems to have a sweet tooth!"

"Good idea," said Dick. "Come on, everyone – you too, Timmy – and not a sound from anyone, mind!"

They went behind the gorse bush and waited. Dick peeped put once or twice, but the bag of barley sugars remained untouched. Then suddenly Timmy gave a low growl, leapt out from behind the gorse bush and ran at something! Everyone followed in excitement. Who was it?

There was nobody there! But up on one of the branches of the nearby tree sat the thief, a barley sugar clutched in his hand, chattering angrily.

"Good GRACIOUS! It's a monkey – a little monkey!" cried George, in the greatest astonishment. "It was he who took the other things! Wherever did he come from?"

The monkey leapt to the top of a broken wall, chattered again at them, and disappeared. Timmy raced to the wall, but the monkey was nowhere to be seen.

52

"Well – what do you think of that?" said Dick. "A monkey! Where has he come from? Somebody must have brought him here – but why? And is that somebody still here – or has he gone?"

"I bet it was that monkey who came and stole my sandal this morning!" said Anne, suddenly.

"Of course!"said Julian. "My word, this is a puzzle! What do we do next?"

"Well, there's one thing we do know – and that is that a monkey wouldn't light a fire or a lamp at night on the island,"said Dick. "That must have been done by a human being – and he MUST still be on the island if his monkey is here. He surely wouldn't go away and leave the little thing to starve."

"Oh, no – it's such a dear little creature," said Anne. "It had a most comical little face – did you notice? Thank goodness it left us most of the barley sugars. Let's have some, before anything else happens!"

They sat sucking the barley sugars, really puzzled. "Buried dog-biscuits!" said Julian. "A monkey that steals food – and sandals! By the way, let's go and have a

look at where we left those dog-biscuits –
maybe they've gone as well!"

They went off to see – but no, there
were the scattered biscuits. Timmy helped
himself to a few again, and a loud
crunching filled the air. The jackdaws
hopped near, hoping to pick up a few
crumbs. Timmy ran at them, and then
stopped and put his nose down to the
ground. He had picked up the same scent
as before!

"Follow the trail again, Tim," said
Julian. "You may do better this time. Go
on!"

But before Timmy could even put his
head down again to follow it, something
peculiar happened. A strange noise came
from the west side of the island – the
miserable howling of a dog!

"That's a dog!" cried Dick, amazed.
"On the island, too – whatever next!
Where is he?"

"Oh, quick – he sounds as if he's in
trouble!" cried George. "What's
happening? Quick, Julian, quick, Timmy!
Oh, poor thing, there he goes, howling
again. We must find him, we must!"

The Five set off in the direction of the
howls, Timmy racing ahead anxiously. He
knew far better than the others that a dog
was in sore trouble – a howling of that kind
meant not only pain, but terror. But how did
a dog come to be on the island – and a
monkey, too! Timmy was as puzzled as the
children.

Julian was now in front of the other
three, and was heading for the seaweed-
spread shore on the west of the island.
George suddenly gave a cry, and pointed.

"There's the monkey again! He's seen
us – he's racing away!"

"Maybe he'll lead us to wherever the
dog is," shouted Julian. The monkey
scampered in front, just ahead of Timmy.
They all came to the shore, and stopped
when they came to the piled-up heaps of
brown, slippery seaweed, covering the
rocks in great masses.

"The dog's stopped howling," said
George, looking all round. "I'm sure he
must be somewhere near here. Hello –
what's the monkey doing? Good gracious –
he's running out over the seaweed. He'll
slip into a pool and drown!"

They watched the tiny brown monkey.

53

He was making his way over the seaweed-covered rocks now, avoiding the pools of water here and there. Further and further out he went. George started to go, too, but Julian pulled her back.

"No. That seaweed is slippery – it's too dangerous to go out on those rocks – we know the sea is very deep in between. Look at that little monkey – where on earth does he think he's going?"

The monkey came to a rock that was absolutely covered with thick masses of seaweed flung there by the surging, wind-blown tide. He had no sooner arrived there than a most extraordinary thing happened!

A small mass of seaweed moved – and out of it came something that made the Five stare in utter disbelief.

"It can't be!" muttered Dick. "No – it can't be!"

It was the brown and white head of a big dog! The Five stared, unable to move. Never had they expected to see such a thing! The head suddenly opened a great mouth and howled dismally! In a trice, Timmy was over the seaweedy rocks,

barking for all he was worth as if to say, "Hold on, friend, I'm coming!"

And then another surprising thing happened! A second head poked up from under a covering of seaweed, and a voice shouted loudly, "Tell your dog to keep off! Mine will fight him! And clear off, all of you!"

The Five were so full of amazement that they stood like dumb creatures, unable to say a word. Then George, afraid that the hidden dog might attack Timmy, yelled to him.

"Tim! Come back! Tim, do you hear me? Heel, Tim, heel!"

Timmy turned, and came back very sulkily, his tail down. Why had George called him back at such an exciting moment? He had only wanted to help the other dog!

The second head was still poking out of its queer sea-weedy hiding place – the head of a small boy! Julian really could not believe his eyes. So that was the hiding-place – under the seaweed – and the dog was

there, too – and probably the monkey had hidden there as well! What was all this going on?

"Hey, you there in the seaweed – come on out!" yelled Julian. "We shan't hurt you. If you want help, we'll give it to you. Come on out, and tell us what you're doing!"

"All right. But if you try to catch me, I'll set my dog on you!" yelled back a defiant voice. "He's a cross-bred Alsatian and he could eat up your dog in a jiffy!"

"We shan't do anything to hurt you or your dog," yelled back Dick. "We heard him howling, poor thing. He's terrified of being under the seaweed. COME ON OUT!"

And then the seaweed pile was heaved up and down, and out came a scraggy, wet boy of about eleven. He pulled the seaweed off the dog, who was quite weighted down by it. The great animal shook itself, and gave one more miserable howl.

"You look out for your dog!" yelled the boy. "Mine's fierce. There'll be a

terrible fight if yours goes for mine."

But Timmy had no idea of fighting such a wet, miserable and hungry dog! He waited until the boy and the Alsatian came scrambling towards the Five, over the rocks, and then he leapt lightly over the seaweed, and ran to the great Alsatian, his long tail wagging in welcome. He whined a little to him, and then licked his face, as if to say, "Cheer up, old fellow! I'm your friend!"

The Alsatian gave a little growl – and then an apologetic bark. He wagged his wet tail, and then, side by side with Timmy, ran up the shore to the waiting children.

The boy came scrambling along, then, the little monkey now chattering on his shoulder, holding on to the boy's hair to save himself from falling. The Five were almost too astonished to say a word, but the two dogs made up for their silence by racing along the beach, barking madly.

The boy looked half-scared, half-sulky, and stared at them defiantly. George spoke to him first.

"What are you doing on my island?"

"Nothing," said the boy. "I just came here – with my dog and monkey – for – well – for a little holiday."

"How did you come here?" asked Julian. "We didn't see any boat."

"I didn't come in a boat," said the boy.

"Well, what did you come in, then?" asked Dick, astonished.

"I shan't tell you," said the boy. "If I did you'd take it away from me – and, and …"

And then, to the dismay of the Five he began to cry bitterly, tears pouring down his cheeks. The little monkey put his arms around the boy's neck and loved him, and the dog leapt up, licking him wherever he could, whining in sympathy.

"Oh, don't cry like that!" said Anne, horrified. She took the boy's hand and led him along the beach. "It's all right. We're your friends. We like your monkey and your dog. Tell us what's the matter. We'll help you!"

Soon they were all sitting down, the monkey still on the boy's shoulder, the dog close beside him. Even Timmy sat as close to the boy as he could, upset because of his tears.

"Have a barley sugar?" said Dick. "Take two. That's right. Now, tell us what's been happening? Why did you come here – and how?"

"There's not much to tell," said the boy. "My name's Bobby Loman. I live with my Granpop in Kirrin Village. My mother and father are dead, and I'm on my own – except for Chippy the monkey here, and Chummy, my Alsatian. I've run away. That's all."

"No,"said Anne gently. "That isn't all. Tell us everything, Bobby."

"Oh, well – it's not much," said Bobby. "Granpop hates Chippy, my monkey, because he steals things. And Chummy costs a lot to keep – and – and – you see, he bit someone last week – and Granpop said he was to be put to sleep. Old Chummy, killed. Why he's my best friend! There's nobody he loves better than me, you don't know how kind and good he is, he sleeps on my bed at night, he licks me when things are bad, he – he …"

Bobby began to cry again, and the Alsatian nestled close to him and licked his cheek.

"See what I mean?" said Bobby. "He loves me! He's the only person who does – and I WON'T have him put to sleep. Well – would you have this nice dog of yours killed?"

"NO! Never, never, NEVER!" said George, and put her arms round a surprised Timmy. "You're quite right to run away, Bobby. I'm GLAD you came to my island. VERY glad. You and Chippy and Chummy can live here as long as you like. We'll bring you food each day, we'll …"

"Steady on, George, old thing," said Julian. "Don't make promises we can't keep. Let's go back to Kirrin Cottage and tell your mother about this – she'll know what's best to do. Bobby can stay with us, perhaps, till things are settled."

"Oh – what fun to have another dog and a monkey, as well as Timmy," said Anne. "Bobby – how did you come to the island, if you didn't have a boat?"

"Oh – that was easy," said Bobby. "I've got one of those floating beds you blow up and Chippy and I sailed on it, with a spade for an oar – and Chummy swam alongside. It's buried in the sand, so that nobody would see it. But I hadn't any food, so …"

"So you crept into our outhouse last night and took a bag of dog-biscuits for Chummy, and some fruit for Chippy," said Julian. "What about yourself?"

"Oh – I've been eating the dog-biscuits," said Bobby. "I took some chocolates too, and ate those. I'm sorry about the stealing. I was sort of – sort of – desperate, you know. I'll pay back for everything I took."

"Come on – let's get back home," said Julian, seeing that Bobby was tired out, cold, wet, and probably very hungry. "Come along now – we'll get our boat!"

The Five went back to where they had left George's boat and took Bobby, Chippy the monkey and Chummy the Alsatian with them. Timmy was very kind to them all, and wagged his tail hard the whole time, to show how friendly he was.

"I'm a bit scared of seeing your Mum and Dad," said Bobby, in the boat. "You're sure they won't send me off to a home – or to prison, or something like that? Chummy

here would fret like anything if I went away from him."

"I don't think you need worry," said Julian, who was rowing. "And I wouldn't be surprised if your Granpop was very pleased to hear you are safe."

Bobby looked doubtful, but said no more. He cuddled up to Timmy and Chummy, who both took turns at licking him. Chippy the monkey was very frisky, and leapt from one person to another, making a funny little chattering noise. He took Dick's handkerchief out of his pocket and pretended to blow his nose on it.

"Hey – you're not to take things from people, I've told you that before!" said Bobby. "Ooooh – that reminds me – he brought this shoe to me this morning – does it belong to any of you?"

And out of his pocket he took – one red sandal! Anne gave a delightful yell.

"OH! It's mine. I missed it this morning. Oh good – now I shan't have to buy a new pair! Chippy – you really are a monkey!"

"There's no doubt about that!" said Dick grinning, and Chippy made his

chattering noise as if he understood every word!

George's mother was most astonished to see a monkey, a dog and another boy added to the Five when they arrived at Kirrin Cottage.

"Who are all these?" she said. "I don't mind the dog, George, but I will not have a monkey running loose in the house."

"He can sleep in the shed, Mother," said George. "Please don't say he can't. Mother, this is Bobby – he ran away from his grandfather who wanted to put his lovely dog to sleep."

"Bobby? Bobby Loman do you mean?" said Mrs Kirrin at once. "Why, he was in the papers today – and a picture of the dog and the monkey too! Bobby, your grandfather is very unhappy and worried. You were a silly little boy to run away just because of an upset. I'm sure your grandfather would never have had your dog destroyed. He only said that in the heat of the moment – when he was very cross!"

Bobby looked rather scared at Mrs. Kirrin's forthright words. George put her arm around his shoulder.

"Mother!" she said, "I'm sure I should run away if you threatened to do anything to Timmy – so I do understand why Bobby ran away to my island. Well – sailed away!"

"Oh – so that's who it was on your island last night!" said Mrs. Kirrin. "Well, well, well! You Five do seem to run into adventure, don't you? How did he get there? And what was the light you saw?"

"I floated there on my air bed," said Bobby. "Oh goodness – I've forgotten it! It's still on the island. The light George saw was my torch, I expect. I was looking for somewhere safe to sleep. I never imagined anyone would see the light of a torch in the dark of midnight!"

"Oh, you don't know George!" said Dick. "If anyone happened to strike even a match on her beloved island, she'd be sure to be looking out of the window at that very moment, and see the flare. Then we'd all have to go rushing off to find out what it was."

"Shut up," said George, crossly. "It's a good thing I did look out of the window

last night – if I hadn't, goodness knows what would have happened to Bobby and the monkey and Chummy – they might have starved to death."

"Well, we still had plenty of dog-biscuits left," said Bobby. "They weren't bad – but awfully hard. I got Chummy to bite them in half for me."

"How very disgusting!" said Mrs. Kirrin. "Now let's think what is best to do. Is your grandfather on the telephone, Bobby? He is? Good. What's his number? I'll ring him up at once, and then you can go home. I hope you'll tell him you're sorry for being such a silly boy!"

"Er, Mother – I've asked Bobby to stay the night," said George. "Mother, the monkey's so sweet. You'll love him. And Chummy is marvellous. You should have seen him with Timmy – they were like old friends at once."

"Very well. Bobby can stay the night," said George's mother, and Bobby beamed all over his face.

"If I had a tail I'd wag it hard," he said, and that made everyone laugh.

58

Things were soon settled. Mrs Kirrin rang up the police to tell them Bobby was safe. Then she rang up his grandfather and told him the news too. The old man was so relieved that he could hardly thank Mrs Kirrin enough.

"I wouldn't have had his dog put to sleep," he said. "I just said that to make Bobby more careful with Chummy. Now that the dog's growing so big and strong, he must be properly trained, and must never bite anyone – Bobby's too easy with him. I'll send the dog to a trainer, and when he comes back he'll be quite all right, and Bobby can have him again."

Bobby didn't think much of this idea when Mrs. Kirrin told him.

"I just won't let Chummy go to a cruel trainer!" he said, looking round at the others for sympathy. But even George rounded on him at once.

"There! You care more for your own feelings than for Chummy's well-being! Don't you want a dog who's safe even with a small child? Don't you want a dog who'll obey you at once, and be a credit to you –

like Timmy is to me?"

"All right, all right. Don't bite my head off. Sounds as if you ought to go to a trainer too!" said Bobby. "Going round snapping at people!"

"Mother! I don't want Bobby to stay the night after all!" said George, fiercely.

"Oh look at that monkey – he's taken a banana from the dish, and he's peeling it just like a human being!" cried Anne, changing the subject very neatly indeed. "Aunt Fanny, do look – isn't he sweet?"

In the end Bobby was allowed to stay the night, and slept downstairs in the kitchen on a couch, with Chippy cuddled beside him, and Chummy on his feet. Upstairs George was in bed with Timmy on her feet, talking about the excitements of the day with Anne.

"How's your tooth?" asked Anne, suddenly remembering the night before, when George had had such bad toothache, and had wandered about the bedroom, and seen a light on Kirrin Island.

"Tooth? What tooth?" said George, surprised. She had quite forgotten all about

it in the excitement of the afternoon. "Oh, the one I had out. Goodness – doesn't it seem AGES since this morning!"

She put her tongue into the space where the tooth had been. "I believe a new one is growing already," she said. "I wish I had teeth like Timmy – snowy white – strong – fierce. I'd like to be able to show all my teeth like Timmy, when I feel really angry!"

Anne laughed. "Well – you almost manage it now," she said. "I say – what's the matter with Timmy? He's pretty restless tonight. Look – he's gone to the door. He wants to go out."

"All he wants is to go and have a talk to Chummy," said George. "All right, Tim. You can go down to the kitchen and sleep with Chummy if you like. I suppose you think he might be lonely. My word – I guess he was scared when he had to hide under that wet, smelly seaweed!"

Timmy pattered down the stairs as soon as the bedroom door was opened. He scraped at the kitchen door and Bobby got up to open it. He was surprised and

pleased to see Timmy, who licked him lavishly, and then went to lie beside the pleased Alsatian. It wasn't often that Timmy had a doggy visitor and he meant to make the most of it!

George took one more look out of the window before she got into bed – and gave a sudden exclamation.

"Anne – I do believe there's a light on Kirrin Island again. Anne – come and look!"

"Don't be an idiot," said Anne, sleepily. "You don't think we're going to start this adventure all over again, do you? It's FINISHED, George, not just beginning. Come back to bed."

George jumped into bed. "It was a light," she said, after a moment or two. "But only a shooting star! What a pity! I'd have liked another adventure – wouldn't you, Anne?"

But Anne was fast asleep, dreaming of monkeys, red sandals, seaweed, big dogs and orange peel. Well – I'm not really surprised at that – are you?

Competition

YOU COULD WIN ALL 21 OF THE BRILLIANT **FAMOUS FIVE** BOOKS IN THIS FREE TO ENTER COMPETITION.

ALL YOU HAVE TO DO IS ANSWER THESE THREE SIMPLE QUESTIONS...

1 When was Enid Blyton born? _____

2 When was the first Famous Five book published? _____

3 Who portrays 'George' in the new Famous Five TV series? _____

WRITE YOUR ANSWERS ON A POSTCARD, OR THE BACK OF A SEALED DOWN ENVELOPE. INCLUDE YOUR NAME, AGE AND ADDRESS, AND POST TO:

Famous Five Competition
Grandreams Limited
Jadwin House
205-211 Kentish Town Road
London NW5 2JU

Closing date for entries is 31st March 1997.

The sender of the first correct entry drawn from the bag on the closing date will receive a complete set of all 21 FAMOUS FIVE BOOKS.

The publishers' decision is final and no correspondence will be entered into.

ANSWERS TO NATURE ZONE QUIZ (PAGE 22)

Score one point for each question, or part of a question, that you answer correctly.
1. Jackdaw, 2. Cod, 3. Stoat, 4. A. Poplar B. Sycamore C. Beech, 5. False: Watermills were used for grinding corn or to drive machinery, 6. Owl, 7. Green, 8. A: to stop cattle crossing, 9. Wind blowing at you from the front, 10. Cow, 11. Right, 12. Dandelion, 13. Horse chestnut, 14. Set, 15. Willow, 16. North, 17. A. Gates B. Crops C. Animals, 18. Ireland, 19. False: Unusual for a conifer tree, the larch loses its leaves, 20. Grass mouse.

HOW DID YOU SCORE?

18–24 points: The Famous Five would definitely ask you along on one of their country walks – your great knowledge would entertain them!

10–17 points: It's clear you have a strong interest in the countryside. Keep it going and you'll become an expert!

Under 10 points: You've probably just started learning about the countryside. Now you've completed this quiz, you'll know more!

Julian and Dick try to ring the old lighthouse bell

George and Uncle Quentin are held to ransom

An escape attempt!

Uncle Quentin congratulates the children